MAGNETISM AND VERY
LOW TEMPERATURES

MAGNETISM AND VERY LOW TEMPERATURES

by

H. B. G. CASIMIR

Philips Research Laboratories
Eindhoven, Holland

DOVER PUBLICATIONS, INC.
NEW YORK

Manufactured in the United States of America

Dover Publications, Inc.
180 Varick Street
New York 14, N. Y.

GENERAL PREFACE

It is the aim of these tracts to provide authoritative accounts of subjects of topical physical interest written by those actively engaged in research. Each author is encouraged to adopt an individualistic outlook and to write the tract from his own point of view without necessarily making it "complete" by the inclusion of references to all other workers or to all allied subjects; it is hoped that the tracts may present such surveys of subjects as the authors might give in a short course of specialized lectures.

By this means readers will be provided with accounts of those subjects which are advancing so rapidly that a full-length book would be out of place. From time to time it is hoped to issue new editions of tracts dealing with subjects in which the advance is most rapid.

M. L. O.
J. A. R.

CONTENTS

heat is developed. In 1926 Debye[10] and Giauque[15] arrived independently at the conclusion, that the demagnetization of a paramagnetic salt might be an extremely suitable process for obtaining very low temperatures. The susceptibility of Gd sulphate had been determined fairly accurately by Woltjer and Kamerlingh Onnes[83] and from their results the heat developed during magnetization could be derived by a simple thermodynamical argument. No estimate could be made at that time of the lowest temperature which can be reached by this method, but it was evident that the temperature would be far below 1° K. In fact, one arrives at the conclusion, that the lowest temperatures, which can easily be reached, will be the temperatures at which Curie's law begins to break down, and no evidence of such a failure is found at ordinary helium temperatures.

1.3. Experimental results.

At the time when Giauque and Debye formulated their proposal, neither of the two had liquid helium at his disposition and it was not until 1933 that the procedure was put on trial. At that time Giauque had built a helium liquefaction plant and all the necessary auxiliary apparatus—including a large kerosene cooled iron free coil for producing the magnetic field. Giauque has stated himself[18] that: "it was evident that the method rested on such a firm thermodynamic basis that all apparatus was designed not merely with the idea of producing low temperatures but to enable other investigations to be carried on in a considerable volume cooled to low temperatures." Giauque's first measurements were carried out with Gd sulphate; later he used various more dilute gadolinium compounds. Together with MacDougall he proceeded to a careful study of the magnetic properties of the salt and tried to establish the thermodynamic scale of temperature below 1° K. The lowest temperature reached in these experiments was of the order of 0·2° K. The susceptibilities were measured by an induction method, using an A.C. bridge.

Some time before the first account of Giauque and MacDougall's results was published[16, 17], de Haas, Wiersma and

Kramers in the Leiden Laboratory had followed up Debye's suggestion (35, 36, 37). By an ingenious adaptation of the magnetic balance, they were able to obtain in a very short time a number of data on various substances. Perhaps the most important result of this series of measurements was, that potassium-chromium alum gives much lower temperatures than the salts of the rare earths. The temperatures were obtained by extrapolating Curie's law; this will of course not give the true thermodynamic temperature but theoretical considerations show, that in this way one will certainly obtain a correct order of magnitude.

De Haas and Wiersma then proceeded to construct apparatus, which would make it possible to cool larger quantities of salt and to study the properties of this salt in very low final fields. Their arrangement was in some respects analogous to that of Giauque, but some additional problems arose because of the fact that it was necessary to move the Dewar vessel out of the big magnet without disconnecting the pumping lines. Susceptibilities were measured with a ballistic galvanometer. With this apparatus very low temperatures were obtained: potassium-chromium alum and iron-ammonium alum gave temperatures of a few hundredths of a degree and with a diluted chromium alum and with caesium-titanium alum temperatures of a few thousandths were reached. Striking though these results may be, the importance of these investigations lies not exclusively in the fact, that these temperatures were obtained: these investigations have also shown the relative merits of a number of substances and provided us with some substances which will make it possible to investigate in more detail the laws of magnetism at very low temperatures.

In the mean time Kürti and Simon had started work on adiabatic demagnetization (56, 57). The main difference between their apparatus and that of Giauque and of de Haas and Wiersma is, that the vessel used for the measurements is directly attached to the liquefier in which a quantity of roughly 100 c.c. of liquid helium is produced by the expansion method. After a summary examination of the properties of iron-ammonium alum, they applied the demagnetization method to the investigation of superconductivity and were able to show, that a number of metals becomes superconductive at temperatures below $1°$K. A valuable addition to the experimental technique was the use of a capsule partly filled with salt and filled with helium at a pressure of a hundred atmospheres at room temperature. This helium becomes liquid at low temperatures and will provide good heat contact between the salt and the capsule and between the salt and some metal embedded in it. In the course of experiments in Paris— where they could use the big magnet of Bellevue—Kürti and Simon made the remarkable discovery, that several salts show an anomaly at very low temperatures, which is in many ways analogous to ferromagnetism. Kürti and Simon have further devoted much attention to the determination of the relation between the "magnetic" temperature obtained by extrapolating Curie's law and the true thermodynamic temperature. As will be described in Chapter IV, this can be done by caloric measurements and here they introduced the method of heating by γ-rays which seems at present to be the only reliable method for specific heat measurements in this region of temperatures. So far only preliminary communications of the results have been published.

Finally it should be mentioned, that also in the Mond Laboratory at Cambridge, work on adiabatic demagnetization has been started. Some of the results obtained will be discussed in Chapter VII.

1.4. Theoretical development.

A few words should now be said concerning the theory of adiabatic demagnetization. Once the problem has been put, it is easy to arrive at a thermodynamic description of the process; the problem can be treated by standard methods and no special difficulties arise. As occasion arose several authors have treated the problem from different points of view. A paper by Debye (11) —being essentially a lecture before the Deutsche Physikalische Gesellschaft—contains a general discussion; Keesom (50) has been the first to formulate clearly a definite procedure for fixing the thermodynamic scale of temperature. The possibility of determining the thermodynamic temperature by magnetic measurements only was emphasized by Giauque, and de Haas and Wiersma have discussed the case of an "ideal" paramagnetic substance in connection with their work on CsTi alum; also in the papers of Simon and his collaborators several thermodynamical results are deduced.

The atomistic theory on the other hand contains many difficult problems. The essential point is, that it is necessary to consider in detail the influence of the magnetic interaction between paramagnetic ions—an effect which can usually be neglected in the study of paramagnetism.

Qualitative considerations may be found in the work of Debye and others; Waller [81] has calculated to a first approximation the specific heat due to magnetic interaction: but the foundations for a systematic quantitative theory are due to Van Vleck [78]. Van Vleck's formulae were applied to the existing experimental material by Hebb and Purcell [48]; somewhat later there appeared a paper by Debye [13] in which the special case of iron-ammonium alum is discussed in a slightly different way. The theory, however, is still far from complete. This is partly due to lack of sufficiently accurate experimental data for fixing certain constants occurring in the theory but also partly to mathematical difficulties. The treatment of Van Vleck is only valid in the limit of (relatively) "high" temperatures; no method has as yet been found for dealing with the temperature region where, according to Simon's measurements, ferromagnetism occurs. Probably an entirely new mathematical procedure will be necessary.

1.5. Scope of present tract.

In this booklet I have tried to give a more or less systematic account of the field of research briefly sketched above. In general I have paid more attention to methods than to results: for though progress has been rapid most results which have been published are of a preliminary nature; accurate experimental data are still scarce. I even fear that in some cases I have given a programme for future work rather than a description of experiments already performed.

In the theoretical discussion of the properties of special salts I have considered mainly certain well established qualitative features. I have restricted myself entirely to salts with a magnetism due to spins only: a discussion of the work of de Haas and Wiersma on cerium and other rare earths will thus be entirely omitted.

As was explained before, many authors have contributed to the thermodynamics of demagnetization, and in formulating this part of the theory, I found it difficult to give accurate references to literature. The treatment of the atomistic theory is mainly based on the work of Van Vleck and Hebb and Purcell. I have tried to explain the fundamental ideas rather than to reproduce the details of the calculation. Special emphasis has been put on certain approximations which hold in the limit of "high" temperatures and which describe the first deviations from "ideal" paramagnetic behaviour. I am convinced that accurate investigations in the region of temperature where these formulae hold will be of great value for the theory of the subject—much in the same way as accurate determinations of the second virial coefficient are of great value for the study of the non-ideal gas.

Chapter II

CLASSICAL THEORY AND EXPERIMENTAL METHODS

2.1. Field equations for a magnetic substance.

The equations for the magnetic field in a space containing non-conducting magnetic substances are

$$\operatorname{curl} B = 4\pi \operatorname{curl} J,$$

and
$$\operatorname{div} B = 0.$$

The physical interpretation of these equations is as follows: in a magnetic body there will exist a magnetic field which will vary from atom to atom; B is the mean value of this microscopic field taken over a small region containing many atoms. The *curl* of B will be proportional to the average value of the current density, which is due to the existence of "Ampère" currents and can be written in the form $\operatorname{curl} J$.

The magnetization J is not uniquely defined; a gradient may be added to it, but usually there is only one natural choice. A vector H may now be introduced by the equation

$$H = B - 4\pi J;$$

it satisfies the equation $\quad \operatorname{curl} H = 0$

and the corresponding boundary conditions. The magnetic behaviour of a substance is characterized by giving the relation between J and H. Of course a relation between any two combinations of the three quantities H, J and B would do just as well. We will see later, that there is sometimes some point in giving the magnetization J as a function of $H + (4\pi/3) J$ instead of giving J as a function of H.

The relation between H and J will in general depend on temperature; in the case of ferromagnetism it depends also on the way in which the state is reached. We will always measure H and B in Gauss: we do not want to make a distinction between

Gauss and Ørstedt. If $J = \chi H$, then the dimensionless constant χ is called susceptibility. We now have

$$B = \mu H,$$

with $$\mu = 1 + 4\pi\chi.$$

2.2. Demagnetization corrections.

Experimental methods will usually give the relation between the exterior field H_0 and the total magnetic moment $M = \iiint J\, dV$ of a body. We will assume that the field H_0 is homogeneous. To put things more rigorously: we assume, that a coil or iron magnet produces in a certain empty region of space a homogeneous field H_0 and we now put a body in this region and measure the moment M. It is essential, that the field producing agents should not be influenced by the presence of the body. In the case of an iron magnet this is not strictly true, since the substance will induce magnetic charges in the pole-pieces, but the effect of these charges is usually very small.

From the relation between M and H_0 we want to find the relation between J and H. If on the other hand the relation between J and H is known, we want to be able to find the relation between M and H_0 for a given experimental arrangement. Now $H \neq H_0$ and the difference can be expressed in terms of J; for a given distribution of J the value of $H - H_0$ can be expressed as an integral. In the case of an ellipsoid and only in this case a homogeneous distribution of J gives rise to a homogeneous field $H_d = H_0 - H$. If J is in the direction of one of the axes, then

$$H_d = \alpha J,$$

but the demagnetization coefficient α is different for the three different axes. Confining ourselves to the case of symmetrical orientation we have

$$H = H_0 - \alpha J,$$

and $$J = M/V,$$

where V is the total volume of the ellipsoid. These equations contain a complete solution of the problem mentioned above.

For a prolate spheroid with axes a and c ($c \geqslant a$), we have

$$\alpha_l = 4\pi \frac{1-e^2}{e^2} \left[\frac{1}{2e} \log \mathrm{nat} \frac{1+e}{1-e} - 1 \right],$$

with

$$e = \left(1 - \frac{a^2}{c^2} \right)^{\frac{1}{2}},$$

if J is parallel to the axis of symmetry, and

$$\alpha_p = 4\pi \left(\frac{1}{2e^2} - \frac{1-e^2}{4e^3} \log \mathrm{nat} \frac{1+e}{1-e} \right)$$

if α_p is perpendicular to this axis. We have

$$2\alpha_p + \alpha_l = 4\pi.$$

For a sphere $\alpha_p = \alpha_l = 4\pi/3$; for an "infinitely long" specimen $\alpha_l = 0$ and $\alpha_p = 2\pi$. Fig. 1 gives a graph of α_l.

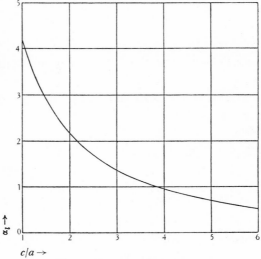

Fig. 1. Demagnetizing factor.

For a body of arbitrary shape we can always calculate a first approximation to the demagnetizing field, by assuming a homogeneous J. A rigorous solution is impossible and the problem is complicated by the fact, that in this case the experimental determinations often do not give the total moment but a more intricate function of the vector J.

2.3. Demagnetization corrections for powders.

In the preceding section we have tacitly assumed that the magnetic substance is a homogeneous body. Experiments are often carried out with more or less densely compressed powders. This makes the calculation of demagnetization corrections rather uncertain. In this section we will use the following symbols:

f: the filling factor = (density powder/density crystal).

V: volume of the body.

M: total magnetic moment.

$J_a = M/V$: average magnetization of the powder.

$J = J_a/f$: average magnetization of crystals.

H_a: average magnetic field in the powder.

H: average field in the crystals.

α_e: demagnetization coefficient belonging to exterior shape of powder.

First of all it is evident, that the mean value of the magnetic field will be given by

$$H_a = H_0 - \alpha_e J_a = H_0 - \alpha_e fJ,$$

but this is not the mean value of the field inside the crystals. That this is the case is best seen by considering a powder consisting of spherical particles. If these particles are very far apart (that is, if f is very small), then we have to apply for each of these particles the demagnetization correction for a sphere. If on the other hand f approaches unity, then H and H_a will be very close together. We have:

$$f \to 1 \qquad H = H_0 - \alpha_e(M/V),$$

$$f \to 0 \qquad H = H_0 - \frac{4\pi}{3}J = H_0 - \frac{4\pi}{3}\frac{1}{f}(M/V).$$

The formula $\quad H = H_0 - \alpha_e(M/V) - \frac{4\pi}{3}\frac{1-f}{f}(M/V) \qquad$ (1)

holds at both limits. Breit (4) has shown that there exists a number of simple models for which this equation holds rigorously. A derivation may also be based on an argument similar to that used in deriving the so-called Lorentz field. However, it is difficult to formulate in a precise way the conditions which a powder must satisfy in order that equation (1) be valid. The equation cannot be considered to be absolutely reliable although it will probably give the right order of magnitude of the corrections which must be applied when f is slightly different from unity. It should further be remembered that, whereas in an ellipsoid the field is strictly homogeneous this will no longer be the case in a powder; this will be very important in cases where J is not a linear function of H.

An extensive and in part rather confusing literature exists in connection with the dielectric constants of mixtures. A survey is given by K. Lichtenecker (70). The question which interests us is whether (1) will hold for salt crystals crushed in a mortar and compressed to a density corresponding to $f = 0.6$, or $f = 0.7$. We do not think that in this respect the existing literature is very helpful.

Special experiments might be performed in order to test equation (1), but it seems more advisable to avoid these difficulties altogether and to use only very dense powders or solid material in all cases where the demagnetization corrections become important.

2.4. Numerical examples.

In order to show the importance of demagnetization corrections we will give a few numerical examples. As a typical substance we may take iron-ammonium alum ($NH_4Fe(SO_4)_2$. $12H_2O$); the susceptibility per gram of this substance is given by $9 \times 10^{-3}/T$, where T is the absolute temperature. The density is 1·71 so that $\chi = 1.54 \times 10^{-2}/T$. At 1° K. the corrections are still quite small: for a sphere $\alpha\chi = 0.066$ and for an ellipsoid with $c/a = 3$ we find $\alpha\chi = 0.021$. If a powder is compressed by hand in a glass tube the filling factor is usually of the order of 2/3;

the demagnetizing field due to the doubtful term in equation 2.3 (1) will then at 1°K. amount to roughly 2 % of the total field.

An entirely different situation is met at temperatures obtained by adiabatic demagnetization. Here χ may easily be as large as 0·5 and the demagnetizing field is of the same order of magnitude as the exterior field. This holds also for the term due to the difference between f and unity. From a mere correction the demagnetizing field has now become an all important factor.

At these extremely low temperatures the magnetic behaviour of a body will depend very strongly on the shape and density; quantitative data will be of very limited value unless dimensions and density are carefully specified.

2.5. Classification of experimental methods.

The methods for determining the magnetic moment of a substance may be divided into two classes: static methods and induction methods. The essential characteristic of the static method is, that during the measurements the magnetic substance remains in a constant magnetic field. The magnetic moment may be determined either by measuring the force on the sample (balance methods) or by measuring the force exerted by the sample on a movable system (magnetometer methods); finally it might also be found from measurements with a flip coil. As far as I know this last method has never been applied to the study of paramagnetism and it does not seem to be very suitable for the purpose, but it has been applied by Meissner and others in work on the magnetic properties of superconductors. In the induction methods on the other hand the exterior field is changed during the measurement; the specimen is surrounded by a coil and when the exterior field is changed an E.M.F. is induced in the coil. This E.M.F. depends on the number of lines of force passing through the coil and thus on the susceptibility of the body. The exterior field may be produced either by the measuring coil itself (measurement of self-inductance) or by another coil (measurement of mutual inductance). The various methods may now be classified in the following way:

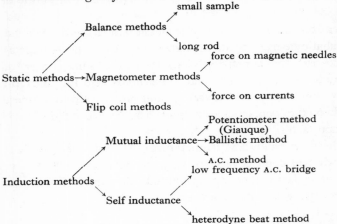

Balance methods
— small sample
— long rod

Magnetometer methods
— force on magnetic needles
— force on currents

Static methods→

Flip coil methods

Mutual inductance→
— Potentiometer method (Giauque)
— Ballistic method

Induction methods

Self inductance
— A.C. method low frequency A.C. bridge
— heterodyne beat method

2.6. Magnetic balances.

For our purpose the most important of the different possible methods is the so-called Faraday method. In this method the specimen is placed in a field which is such that H_0 does not vary appreciably inside the body, but which is, on the other hand, sufficiently inhomogeneous to exert a measurable force. These two conditions can usually be satisfied only by taking a small sample. If M is the magnetic moment, then the force will be given by

$$K = (M \, \mathrm{grad}) \, H_0.$$

Let us suppose that H_0 and M have the direction of the x-axis, then

$$K_x = M_x \frac{\partial H_x^0}{\partial x},$$

$$K_y = M_x \frac{\partial H_y^0}{\partial x} = M_x \frac{\partial H_x^0}{\partial y}.$$

It will now depend on the magnet used whether the inhomogeneity is parallel to the field or perpendicular to the field. If an ordinary magnet of the Weiss type is used, the situation is usually as shown in fig. 2 and the force is in the direction of the vertical. In the measurements of the Leiden school (cf. (82)) the sample is suspended on one end of the beam of a balance; the other end carries a coil which is connected in series with a fixed coil. The balance is brought in equilibrium by adjusting the current through these coils. A mirror is mounted on the beam of the balance and the position of the balance can be read on a scale.

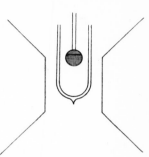

Fig. 2. · Faraday method.

Provided carefully calibrated ammeters are used for measuring the compensation currents the force can fairly easily be determined to two parts in a thousand, but there are several factors which tend to make the determination of magnetic moments much less accurate. Although some susceptibilities have been determined with an accuracy of a few parts in a thousand at hydrogen temperatures, the accuracy of the best published measurements in the helium region is not better than 2 or 3 %.

Sucksmith uses a sensitive spring balance consisting of a phosphor-bronze ring on which two mirrors are mounted, instead of the rather elaborate Leiden apparatus. Especially in cases where a large number of samples of approximately the same susceptibility must be measured the Sucksmith balance is very useful.

The two most important disadvantages of the method are firstly, that in order to have always the same value of H_0 and $\partial H_0/\partial x$ the place of the sample must be very accurately known, and secondly, that the arrangement has a tendency to become unstable with respect to sideways displacements. This last feature will probably be eliminated by using magnets of the cylindrical coil type such as have been constructed by Bitter and by Ashmead in the Mond Laboratory.

An alternative method is the Gouy method. Here the specimen is a long cylindrical rod; the lower end is in the middle of the homogeneous field, the upper end in a place where the field is small. If the moment is proportional to the field strength, then the force is given by $\frac{1}{2}\chi(H_0{}^2 - H_1{}^2)$. The advantage of this method is that the force does not depend appreciably on position, and that a calibration of only two values of the field is required. But it is restricted to cases where M/H is constant. For most of the work on magnetism at low temperatures it is therefore unsuitable. On the other hand it is one of the best methods for determining very small susceptibilities. It has recently been applied by Schubnikow for investigating the paramagnetism of hydrogen, which is due to the nuclear spin.

2.7. Magnetometers.

Magnetometers consisting of a system of magnetic needles have been used in the study of ferromagnetism but the author is not aware of any application to low temperature physics (apart from some measurements by de Haas and Mrs Casimir on persisting currents in superconductors). The instrument may easily be made very sensitive. On the other hand it is of no use for measurements in a wide range of exterior fields and though it might prove valuable for certain special investigations it does not appear to be of much use for the type of measurement which will be discussed mainly in this tract.

Another possibility is to measure the force exerted on a system of coils instead of a system of needles. An ingenious magnetometer based on this method has been developed by Schultz in the Leiden Laboratory and been applied to the determination of magnetic moments in exterior fields up to a few thousand Gauss. For a description of this apparatus we refer to the paper of Schultz which is to appear shortly.

2.8. Induction methods; ballistic methods.

If a magnetic substance is surrounded by a measuring coil and a field coil producing a homogeneous field H_0, then the number of lines of force passing through the measuring coil will be given by an equation of the form

$$N_m = OH_0 + OGM,$$

where O is the total area of the measuring coil, M the magnetic moment and G a geometric factor. This equation is based on the assumption, that the magnetization is homogeneous, otherwise the product GM has to be replaced by an integral.

There are now different possibilities for measuring N_m, but they are all based on the fact that an E.M.F. is induced in the measuring coil when N_m is changed.

In some of their experiments Giauque and MacDougall [20] have determined the magnetic moment of a substance at very low temperature in the following way: H_0 was kept constant, but by admitting a minute quantity of gas the temperature was slowly raised, and the moment M dropped to a value close to zero. This decrease of M took place so slowly, that the E.M.F. could be read as a function of time with an ordinary galvanometer. The value of $\Delta N_m = OGM$ could then be determined by integration.

De Haas and Wiersma [43] and also Kürti and Simon [59] have used a ballistic method. If the field H_0 is reversed by reversing the current in the field coil, then N_m will be changed to $-N_m$. Now at ordinary helium temperatures OGM will be rather small compared to OH_0. It is therefore necessary to compensate this number of lines of force. This can easily be done by connecting measuring coil and field coil in series with the secondary and primary of some form of mutual inductance, which is adjusted to such a value that the throw corresponding to the empty coil is almost compensated. By short circuiting the field coil and reversing a small current in the primary of the mutual inductance the sensitivity of the galvanometer can be calibrated. The throw corresponding to the empty coil is usually not exactly compensated and determined by carrying out measurements at different temperatures and extrapolating to high temperatures $(1/T \to 0)$, where M becomes zero. The method is easy to set up and for measurements in and below the helium region sufficient sensitivity can easily be obtained. In ordinary measurements 10 lines of force is usually the lowest value of the flux which can be observed. With a measuring coil of 2000 turns, a measuring field of 25 G. and a specimen in the form of a long cylinder with a cross section of 4 sq. cm. a change of susceptibility of 0.4×10^{-5} can then be measured. The accuracy of the results depends mainly on the constancy of the geometry of the coils. The ballistic method will give the value of OGM only if the time the moment requires to change from M to $-M$ is short compared to the period of the galvanometer; for a long period galvanometer this is no serious restriction: the ballistic method is almost a static method.

2.9. A.C. methods.

Instead of measuring the mutual inductance by the ballistic method we may also use some form of A.C. bridge. This has several advantages: it is easy to obtain a higher sensitivity than with the ballistic method, the determinations can be made in a much shorter time, the galvanometer is continuously observed, and

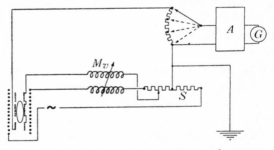

Fig. 3. Circuit for determination of mutual inductance.

finally, the value of the mutual inductance can be read directly on a standard variable inductance, so that no calculations are required. An extremely convenient bridge method is the so-called Hartshorn method, and the author is indebted to Dr Snoek of the Philips Laboratory and to Dr Shire of the Mond Laboratory who both drew his attention to the advantages of this arrangement, which has already been applied by Dr Shire for work on magnetism at very low temperatures (paper read at the Cambridge Meeting of the British Association). A diagram of the circuit now used in the Leiden Laboratory is shown in fig. 3. The measuring coil consists of three sections, the upper and the lower one having each half the number of turns of the one in the middle. The mutual inductance is therefore zero, or at least very small, when no salt is present. This will improve the accuracy of the measurements for several reasons and it will reduce magnetic pick-up to a minimum which is especially important when working at mains frequency. M_v is a variable mutual inductance; four-dial mutual inductance boxes can be obtained commercially and are also fairly easy to construct. S is a slide wire and may be replaced by any form of potentiometer; this arrangement is necessary in order to compensate that part of the secondary voltage that is in phase with the primary current. These "impurities" are due to eddy currents and capacities but are small unless the capacities are exceptionally large; the first factor is usually the most important at 50 cycles. The most convenient detecting device is an amplifier connected to a vibration galvanometer, which can be fairly insensitive. It is necessary that the capacitance between primary and secondary should be very small and a screen may be inserted between them, but all other capacities as well as eddy currents have in first approximation no influence on the setting of M_v but only on the setting of S. A phase angle of 10^{-3} gives rise to an error of the order of one part in two millions in the value of the mutual inductance, and in most measurements phase angles of 10^{-2} can be tolerated. The method is not very suitable for the measurement of very small phase angles; for that purpose a method using a more elaborate earthing device would be necessary; but for measuring phase angles of a few times 10^{-2} it is fairly useful, although the equilibrium conditions become frequency dependent.

Of course the values obtained by an A.C. method will only be equal to those which would follow from static measurements when equilibrium is reached in a time short compared with the period. In Chapter VII we will discuss the effects which will occur whenever this is not the case.

Giauque and MacDougall in their work on gadolinium salts, have invariably used an Anderson bridge for measuring the self inductance of a coil surrounding the substance. Very accurate

results were obtained and the method appears to be entirely satisfactory for most purposes. Still we believe, that in principle the
mutual inductance method is superior. In the first place the measuring field in the self inductance method will only be homogeneous when the coil is long compared with the specimen, and
at temperatures where the demagnetization corrections become
important it is very important that this condition is fulfilled. But
this will appreciably reduce the geometric factors and therefore the
relative sensitivity. In the second place it is not possible to use an
"astatic" coil; in order to avoid pick-up it is therefore necessary
carefully to eliminate stray fields and to work at a frequency incom-
mensurable with mains frequency. Finally, whereas in the case
of mutual inductances changes of eddy currents and capacitances
will only in second approximation affect the value of the mutual
inductance, they will have a first order influence on the self
inductance.

A very accurate method for determining the coefficient of self
inductance is the heterodyne beat method. It was applied by
Gorter and Brons in their work on paramagnetic relaxation.

2.10. Induction measurements in exterior fields.

With the balance the magnetic moment of a substance can be
measured in a widely varying range of values of the exterior field.
In this respect the possibilities of the induction methods would
at first sight appear to be rather limited and it seems worth while
to investigate this question in more detail. First of all the measuring field may be changed and in this way M can be determined
as a function of H_0. With the mutual inductance methods this
may be done in fields up to a few hundred Gauss; with the self
inductance method only very small fields can be used. We may
now superimpose a constant external field H_e and have to consider two possibilities.

(a) H_e and H_0 are parallel; then if $H_0 \ll H_e$ the induction
method will give the value of $\partial M/\partial H$. If measurements of this
type are made at a number of values of the external field, M as a
function of H can be derived by integration. The method was

used by Giauque; it cannot easily be used in external fields produced by an iron magnet.

(b) H_e is perpendicular to H_0. We put $H_e = H_x$ and $H_0 = H_y$. If again $H_0 \ll H_e$, then the reversing of H corresponds to a rotation of the exterior field over an angle H_0/H_e. If the substance is isotropic and spherical then also the magnetic moment will be rotated over this same angle.

We have
$$\frac{M_x}{M_y} = \frac{H_x}{H_y},$$

and, since the induction methods give us directly the value of M_y/H_y, we have a method to determine M_x. For a spheroid demagnetization corrections must be applied; a simple calculation yields
$$\frac{M_x}{H_x} = \frac{M_y/H_y}{1 + (\alpha_x - \alpha_y)(M_y/H_y)/V}.$$

As far as I know this procedure has not been described before. It can also be applied when H_e is produced by an electromagnet, but in that case it is necessary to study in some detail the influence of the pole-pieces on the field H_0. The method was used by de Haas and the author in the course of some preliminary experiments on iron-ammonium alum; we believe that it may prove very useful for studying magnetic moments in fields between 50 and 1000 G.

2.11. Fundamental thermodynamical relations.

The first law of thermodynamics can be written in the following form:
$$dQ = dU - H_0 dM, \qquad (1)$$
where dQ is the heat supplied to the body and dU the change of internal energy. In order to prove this equation one has to show that the external work done by the sources of the field is given by $+H_0 dM$. This can easily be proved for a field produced by a coil: if M changes by dM an electromotive force is induced in this coil, this will temporarily decrease the Joule heat developed in the coil whereas the work done by the batteries remains the same. A simple calculation shows that the difference is equal to $H_0 dM$.

Besides the function U we will also introduce a function E defined by

$$E = U - H_0 M,$$

so that

$$dQ = dE + M\,dH_0;$$

it depends entirely on the problem under investigation which of the two functions is the more useful. Personally we prefer always to use (1) as the starting point for purely thermodynamical considerations.

One might be tempted to ask which is now the true energy, U or E, but to this question no unique answer can be given. The system consisting of magnet + batteries + substance has a well-defined energy, but it is a matter of taste whether the term $H_0 M$, which can be regarded as part of the field energy, will be included in the energy of the salt or not.

By applying the second law of thermodynamics we find

$$\left(\frac{\partial U}{\partial H}\right)_T = \left(T\frac{\partial M}{\partial T} + H\frac{\partial M}{\partial H}\right).$$

This important formula enables us to calculate U in an arbitrary field when $U(H = 0, T)$ and the magnetization curves at different temperatures are known. For dQ we find

$$dQ = \left\{\left(\frac{\partial U}{\partial T}\right)_H - H\left(\frac{\partial M}{\partial T}\right)_H\right\} dT + T\left(\frac{\partial M}{\partial T}\right)_H dH.$$

The total heat supplied to the body during isothermal magnetization is thus given by

$$\Delta Q = T\int_0^H \left(\frac{\partial M}{\partial T}\right)_H dH,$$

and for the entropy we have

$$S(H, T) - S(0, T) = \int_0^H \frac{\partial M}{\partial T} dH.$$

We will treat two examples:

(a) M does not depend on the temperature. Then

$$\left(\frac{\partial U}{\partial H}\right)_T = H\frac{\partial M}{\partial H},$$

and

$$\Delta Q = 0.$$

No heat is developed when the substance is magnetized.

(b) The ideal paramagnetic case, $M = f(H/T)$. In this case we have

$$\left(\frac{\partial U}{\partial H}\right)_T = 0;$$

therefore

$$dQ = -H\,dM,$$

and

$$S(H,T) = S(0,T) - \frac{1}{T}\int H\,dM.$$

Heat is liberated during the magnetization process and the entropy is lowered.

We will in the following always measure energies either in ergs or in watt-seconds, and usually also express specific heats and entropies in the corresponding units.

As a matter of fact we believe that the calory, though being a useful unit for steam engines and central heating plants, ought to be abandoned entirely in low temperature work.

Chapter III

QUANTUM THEORY OF PARAMAGNETISM

3.1. Hamiltonian and partition function.

In this chapter we will briefly summarize the theory of paramagnetism in so far as it will be required for understanding the
properties of those substances which are most useful in demagnetization experiments. For a thorough discussion of the
fundamental principles and of applications to a much wider variety
of substances the reader is referred to the books of Van Vleck [77]
and Stoner [76]. An introduction to the subject is also contained
in Wiersma's dissertation [82] whereas Gorter's dissertation [22]
contains a useful summary of experimental results. We will first
treat the case in which the atoms in a paramagnetic salt are independent of one another. Each atom can be described by a Hamiltonian which contains the magnetic field H_0 as a parameter and
the Hamiltonian of the system as a whole is equal to $\Sigma \mathcal{H}$. The
value of the Hamiltonian is not equal to the energy U introduced
in section 2.11 but to the quantity $E = U - H_0 M$. We will not
prove that this is the case, but perhaps the following simple
argument will help to make plausible this fact. Let us suppose
that by some force K work is done on a system in a constant
magnetic field. If now this force produces also a change in
magnetic moment, then the change of U is not equal to the work
done by K, since the work $H_0 dM$ is as it were automatically done
by the coil producing the field; it follows that the work done by
K is equal to the increase of E. To determine the magnetic properties of an assembly of atoms we have to proceed in the
following way. First we have to find the characteristic values of
the Hamiltonian, or in other words the energy levels of the atom,
E_n. Next we must calculate the partition function

$$Z = \Sigma e^{-E_n/kT},$$

where k, Boltzmann's constant, is equal to $1 \cdot 37 \times 10^{-16}$. Once Z

has been found, the entropy, energy and magnetic moment can easily be determined.

We have
$$E = NkT^2 \frac{\partial}{\partial T}(\log Z) \left.\phantom{\frac{\partial}{\partial T}}\right\}$$
$$M = NkT \frac{\partial}{\partial H}(\log Z) \left.\phantom{\frac{\partial}{\partial T}}\right\} \tag{1}$$
$$S = Nk \frac{\partial}{\partial T}(T \log Z) \left.\phantom{\frac{\partial}{\partial T}}\right\}$$

where N is the number of atoms. If all quantities are calculated for a gram atom Nk is equal to the gas constant $R = 8 \cdot 31$ watt sec./degree (or $1 \cdot 98$ cal./degree). The index of H has been omitted.

Of course the relation
$$T dS = dE + M dH$$
is identically fulfilled.

3.2. Simplification of general formulae.

For all paramagnetic ions discussed in this tract the distribution of energy levels is such that there is a small number of levels very near the lowest level. The distance does not exceed $k \times 1° K.$; all other levels lie at a distance $\gg kT$, where T is a temperature in the liquid helium or liquid hydrogen region. The expression for the partition function can now be simplified; we have only to sum over the lowest levels E_a.

Let us call $E_a{}^0$ the energy of the lowest levels in zero field and $\psi_a{}^0$ the corresponding wave-functions. To find the energy levels in a field H (in the direction of the z-axis) we must first determine the eigen values $E_{a, H}{}^{(1)}$, of the (finite) matrix
$$\| E_a{}^0 \delta_{ab} - H \mu_{ab}{}^z \|,$$
where $\qquad \mu_{ab}{}^z = \int (\psi_a{}^0)^* \mu^z \psi_b{}^0 \, dx$

are the matrix-elements of the magnetic moment. If the levels are strictly degenerate this matrix is simply equal to $-(H \cdot \mu)$ and if the states correspond to a definite angular momentum the energy levels can be found from the well-known vector diagram.

But the energies E_a are not exactly equal to these values $E_{a,\,H}^{(1)}$. Two corrections must be added: a diamagnetic correction

$$\Delta_1 E_a = \frac{e^2 H^2}{8mc^2} \underset{i}{S} (R_i{}^2 - z_i{}^2)_{aa},$$

where $\underset{i}{S}$ is the sum over all electrons (R_i radius vector, z_i z-coordinate of ith electron), and a term due to the existence of the higher levels. This last term will only exist when the magnetic moment μ has non-diagonal elements, $\mu_{ar}{}^z$ (r is one of the higher levels). In that case we find a second order correction to the energy

$$\Delta_2 E_a = -\sum_r \frac{H^2 |\mu_{ar}{}^z|^2}{\delta_{ar}},$$

where δ_{ar} is the energy difference $E_r - E_a$; in consequence of our assumptions δ_{ar} may be assumed to be independent of a. For all the paramagnetic ions, which will be discussed in the following, it can be shown that both $\Delta_1 E_a$ and $\Delta_2 E_a$ do not depend on a.

Therefore we have

$$\log Z = -(\Delta_1 E + \Delta_2 E)/kT + \log Z_1,$$

where Z_1 is calculated with the values $E_{a,\,H}^{(1)}$. The extra term in $\log Z$ does not lead to an additional entropy but it leads to an additional magnetic moment

$$\Delta M = -\frac{Ne^2 H}{4mc^2} \underset{i}{S} (R_i{}^2 - z_i{}^2)_{aa} + 2H\sum_r \frac{|\mu_{ar}{}^z|^2}{\delta_{ar}}.$$

The first term is the so-called diamagnetic term, the second term shows the existence of temperature independent paramagnetism. In our subsequent considerations these terms need not be taken into account. In the first place they are very small compared with the paramagnetic terms at low temperatures; further they have no influence on the thermodynamic behaviour, and finally they are automatically eliminated from the magnetic measurements when an induction method is used, since in these methods the correction for the empty coil is always determined by extrapolating to $T \to \infty$. The readings of a ballistic galvanometer (or the settings of an A.C. bridge) corrected in this way, will only give the moment due to Z_1 and will not include the temperature independent terms.

3.3. Magnetism due to electron spins.

Our discussion will now be restricted to salts for which the lowest states are very simple. Apart from small splittings, the influence of which will be discussed in the next section, they correspond to the free orientation of a spin-vector, being the resultant of 7, 5, 3 or 1 parallel electron spins, so that the total angular momentum in units $\hbar$ is $7/2$, $5/2$, $3/2$ or $1/2$. The magnetic moment corresponding to each spin is—at least with a fair degree of approximation—the Bohr magneton, $\mu_B = e\hbar/2mc$. The typical representatives of these four cases are gadolinium (7 spins), trivalent iron (5 spins), trivalent chromium (3 spins) and trivalent titanium (1 spin). Let us first consider the case $S = \frac{1}{2}$. In a magnetic field two orientations are possible with energy $+H\mu_B$ and $-H\mu_B$. Therefore

$$Z = e^{+H\mu_B/kT} + e^{-H\mu_B/kT}.$$

It follows that

$$S = Nk\left[{}^e\log 2 \operatorname{Ch}\left(\frac{H\mu_B}{kT}\right) - \frac{H\mu_B}{kT}\operatorname{Tgh}\left(\frac{H\mu_B}{kT}\right)\right],$$

and

$$M = N\mu_B \operatorname{Tgh}\frac{H\mu_B}{kT}.$$

For low fields

$$M = N\frac{\mu_B^2}{kT}H,$$

and hence

$$\chi_A = \frac{N}{kT}\mu_B^2 = \frac{(N\mu_B)^2}{(Nk)T},$$

where χ_A is the susceptibility per gram ion. To obtain χ we have to multiply by the density ρ and to divide by the molecular weight (divided by the number of ions per molecule) A. The susceptibility obeys Curie's law; more generally M is a function of (H/T).

For a spin angular momentum s we have $(2s+1)$ states with energies

$$2sH\mu_B,\ (2s-2)H\mu_B,\ \ldots,\ -2sH\mu_B.$$

The most convenient expression for the entropy is

$$S/R = \alpha \operatorname{Coth} \alpha - (2s+1)\alpha \operatorname{Coth}(2s+1)\alpha + {}^e\!\log \frac{\operatorname{Sh}(2s+1)\alpha}{\operatorname{Sh}\alpha},$$

where
$$\alpha = \frac{H\mu_B}{kT} = 0.67 \times 10^{-4} \frac{H}{T}.$$

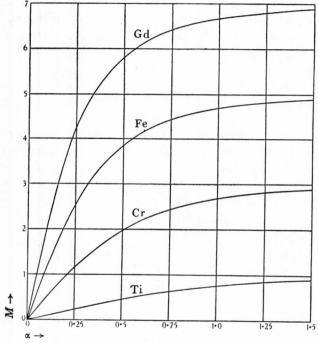

Fig. 4. Magnetization (in units $N\mu_B$) as a function of $\alpha = \dfrac{H\mu_B}{kT}$.

With suitable tables values of S can be calculated very quickly. The author found the tables of Milne-Thomson and Comrie [72] extremely convenient for this purpose.

The magnetic moment is given by

$$M = (2s+1)\operatorname{Coth}(2s+1)\alpha - \operatorname{Coth}\alpha.$$

For the susceptibility per gram ion we find

$$\chi_A = \operatorname*{Lim}_{H\to 0} \frac{M}{H} = \frac{4\mu_B{}^2 N}{3kT} s(s+1),$$

or, inserting numerical values,

$$\chi_A = \frac{1}{T} \times 0.372^4 \times \frac{4s(s+1)}{3}.$$

The additive constant in the entropy is chosen in such a way, that in high fields $S = 0$, which is a reasonable choice since in that case only one state is possible. In zero fields we have

$$S(H = 0) = Nk^e\log(2s+1)$$

corresponding to the fact, that all $2s+1$ states are equally probable. The decrease of entropy in an exterior field is due to the

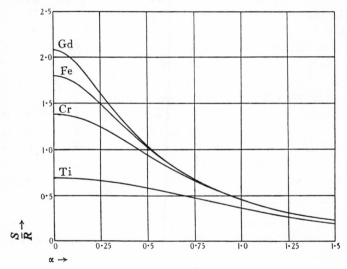

Fig. 5. Entropy (in units R) as a function of α.

fact that the uniform distribution over these $2s+1$ states is modified. It follows from our formula that also at the absolute zero $S = Nk^e\log(2s+1)$ in zero field. This is due to our assumption that the levels are strictly degenerate. In reality this will of course never be the case.

In low fields ($\alpha \ll 1$) we can write

$$S = S_0 - \tfrac{1}{2}\chi_A \frac{H^2}{T}.$$

Fig. 4 shows the magnetization curves for 7, 5, 3 and 1 spin ($N\mu_B$ is chosen as unit). The entropy (in units $Nk = R$; $R = 8\cdot31$ watt sec./degree) is shown in fig. 5. It will be seen that for $\alpha > 1$ the entropies of Gd, Fe and Cr are practically identical. Further the difference in entropy change produced by the field is not very large: for Gd it is only about 50 % higher than for Cr (for small values of α on the other hand, Gd and Cr differ by a factor $4\cdot2$). The entropy change for Ti, however, is about three times smaller.

3.4. Influence of splittings.

In reality the $(2s + 1)$ levels will not be degenerate. The question arises as to how far the results of the preceding section will be influenced by the existence of these separations. The answer is, that these splittings have no influence at all as long as they are small compared with kT. When they become comparable with kT of course a special investigation is necessary.

The result is an almost immediate consequence of a theorem which states, that the diagonal sum of any matrix is an invariant for canonical transformations (or in other words, that this diagonal sum does not change when the wave-functions undergo a linear transformation). The energy values are obtained by transforming

$$\mathscr{H}_{ab} = \| E_a \delta_{ab} - H\mu_{ab}{}^z \|$$

to diagonal form. The partition function Z is the diagonal sum of $\exp(-\mathscr{H}/kT)$ and since this diagonal sum is an invariant we can also write

$$Z = \sum_a (e^{-\mathscr{H}/kT})_{aa}.$$

But this can be expanded in a series

$$Z = \sum_a (e^{-H\mu/kT})_{aa} + O\left(\frac{A}{kT}\right) f\left(\frac{H\mu}{kT}\right),$$

where A is a measure for the total separation of the levels. To a first approximation, the partition function is the same as in the case when there are no separations at all, and this result does not depend on the value of $H\mu$, which can be either large or small compared with the separations. The influence of the separations can be developed in a series of powers of $1/T$. The susceptibility for instance will be given by a formula of the type

$$\chi = \frac{a}{T}\left(1 + \frac{B}{T} + \frac{C}{T^2} + \ldots\right),$$

often, as will be explained in Chapter v, the coefficient B will vanish.

By way of illustration we will consider in more detail a very simple example. Let us consider the case of one spin. If we first assume that the levels are strictly degenerate, then in a field H_z there will be two levels. These levels have a magnetic moment μ^z in opposite directions, but because of the energy difference $2\mu H$ one level is slightly more occupied than the other, the difference being proportional to $N\mu H/kT$. In this way there results a moment proportional to $N\mu^2 H/kT$. When the field is changed the moment μ of each level remains unchanged. What does change is the distribution of atoms over these levels. Now let us make a different assumption and suppose that the levels are separated, the energy difference being Δ and the wave-functions ψ_a and ψ_b and let us suppose that μ^z has no diagonal elements. If a small field ($H\mu \ll \Delta$) is applied, the distance Δ is to a first approximation not affected. But, due to the non-diagonal elements of μ, the wave-functions are modified:

$$\psi_a{}' = \psi_a + \frac{H\mu_{ba}}{\Delta}\psi_b,$$

$$\psi_b{}' = \psi_b - \frac{H\mu_{ab}}{\Delta}\psi_a$$

(we assume $E_a < E_b$ and $\Delta > 0$). In consequence both states will have a magnetic moment:

$$\int (\psi_a{}')^*\mu\psi_a{}'\,dx = 2\frac{H\,|\,\mu_{ab}\,|^2}{\Delta}; \quad \int (\psi_b{}')^*\mu\psi_b{}'\,dx = -2\frac{H\,|\,\mu_{ab}\,|^2}{\Delta}.$$

The induced magnetic moments have opposite sign. Now the upper and lower levels are not equally occupied; the surplus in the lower state is proportional to $N\Delta/kT$.

It follows, that there will be an induced moment proportional to $(H \mid \mu_{ab} \mid^2/\Delta) N\Delta/kT$ and our general theorem states, that this is equal to the result obtaining when there are no separations; of course this can also easily be shown by a direct calculation. The remarkable point, however, is that in this case the distribution of atoms is unchanged and that the moment is due to polarization. The mechanism of the magnetization is different from the mechanism in the case of free ions, and we will later find cases where this is important, even at temperatures for which the influence of the splittings on the magnetic behaviour can be neglected.

If on the other hand $H\mu \gg \Delta$, then the energy levels and wave-functions will be the same as for a free atom (Paschen-Back effect). In such fields the magnetism will again be due to the mechanism described for the case $\Delta = 0$.

3.5. Interaction between atoms.

The atoms of a solid are not completely independent of one another. In order to treat the general case we have to proceed as follows: we must first determine the energy levels of the system as a whole, which are the eigen values of the Hamiltonian of the total system, and then calculate

$$z = \Sigma e^{-E_n/kT}.$$

The entropy, energy and magnetic moment are again given by

$$\left. \begin{aligned} S &= k\frac{\partial}{\partial T}(T \log z) \\ M &= k\frac{\partial}{\partial H}(T \log z) \\ E &= kT^2 \frac{\partial}{\partial T}(\log z) \end{aligned} \right\}. \tag{1}$$

If the atoms are independent, the Hamiltonian is the sum of the Hamiltonians for the separate atoms and we have

$$z = Z^N,$$

so that (1) reduces to 3.1 (1). Though this will no longer be valid when interactions between ions are taken into account, it remains true that for large N and for a definite arrangement of ions in a crystal lattice and for a definite shape of the sample of matter $\log z$ is proportional to N, or in other words,

$$\underset{N \to \infty}{\text{Lim}} \frac{1}{N} \log z = -kT\psi,$$

where ψ, the free energy per ion, does not depend on N.

Many of the simplifications discussed above are still possible, while it is only necessary to sum over the lowest levels. Again there will be a diamagnetic and a temperature independent paramagnetic term which can be neglected in our problem.

The argument of 3.4 can easily be adopted to show, that for $T \gg \tau$, where τ is a measure for the separations, the splittings have no influence on the magnetization and the entropy.

Thus the interaction becomes of importance only at low temperatures. For the case in which the lowest state of each atom is twofold degenerate for instance, the lowest state of the whole system would be 2^N-fold degenerate. Due to the interaction these 2^N states will spread out in a band. The width of this band can be described by a temperature τ; in Chapter v we will have to consider what will happen when T is no longer very large compared with τ.

Chapter IV

EXPERIMENTS ON ADIABATIC DEMAGNETIZATION

4.1. Principle of method.

In 3.3 we have discussed the decrease of entropy caused by magnetization. If a substance is at a temperature T and a field is applied, then heat is developed. If this heat is carried away there results a state of lower entropy than the initial state. If then the field is switched off and no heat is supplied the entropy will remain constant. There will result a state in zero field with lower entropy than the initial state and therefore a state of lower temperature.

Let $S(o, T_1)$ be the entropy in the initial state, then

$$S(H_1, T_1) = S(o, T_1) + \int_0^{H_1} \frac{\partial M}{\partial T} dH.$$

The state of equal entropy in a field $H_2 < H_1$ will be a state of lower temperature, $T_2 < T_1$, and we will have

$$S(H_2, T_2) = S(o, T_1) + \int_0^{H_2} \frac{\partial M}{\partial T} dH.$$

In the special case when $H_2 = o$ we have

$$S(o, T_2) = S(H, T_1).$$

On the other hand

$$S(o, T_2) = S(o, T_1) - \int_{T_2}^{T_1} \frac{C_p}{T} dT,$$

where C_p is the specific heat. Hence

$$\int_{T_2}^{T_1} \frac{C_p}{T} dT = - \int_0^{H_1} \left(\frac{\partial M}{\partial T} \right)_{T=T_1} dH.$$

4.2. Adiabatic demagnetization at helium and hydrogen temperatures.

We will first discuss an example where both the entropy and the susceptibility as a function of temperature are known; the best substance for this purpose is Gd sulphate. The susceptibility follows Curie's law. According to measurements of Clark and Keesom (8) (compare also 6.5) the specific heat of 1 gram ion of this substance can be represented in the temperature region between 1·5 and 20° K. with a fair degree of accuracy by

$$C_p = \frac{2 \cdot 34}{T^2} + 1 \cdot 21 \times 10^{-3} T^3 \text{ watt sec./degree,}$$

and hence

$$\int_{T_2}^{T_1} \frac{C_p}{T} dT = 1 \cdot 17 \left(\frac{1}{T_2^2} - \frac{1}{T_1^2} \right) + 4 \times 10^{-4} (T_1^3 - T_2^3).$$

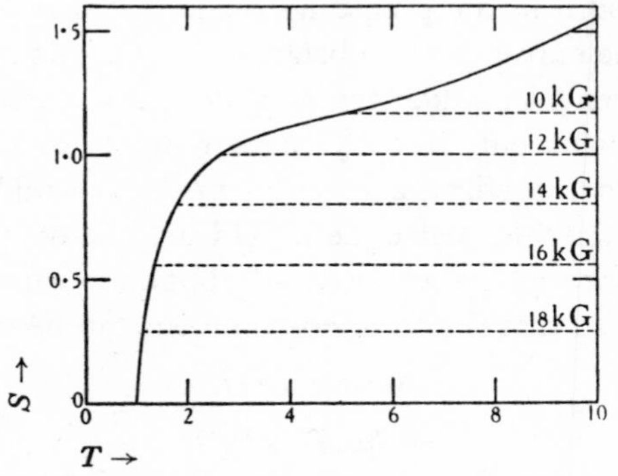

Fig. 6. The entropy of Gd sulphate as a function of temperature.

This entropy is shown in fig. 6; the entropy at 1° K. has been put equal to zero (but it should be remembered, that between 1·0 and 1·5° K. the curve will not correctly represent the entropy).

The change of entropy due to magnetization in a field which does not produce saturation is

$$\Delta S = \frac{1}{T} \times \tfrac{1}{2} \chi_A H^2 = 3 \cdot 91 \times \frac{H^2}{T^2} \times 10^{-7} \text{ watt sec./degree;}$$

the entropies at 10° K. for different values of H are also shown in the diagram. The final temperatures corresponding to an initial state of 10° K. in a field H can now at once be read from the diagram. Starting from 10° K. and a field of 13,000 G. we would for instance arrive at a temperature of 2° K.

On the other hand, by determining the final temperatures corresponding to given initial conditions, one can derive the entropy diagram. The interesting feature of such a determination, as compared with the usual caloric measurements, is that the body itself can serve as a thermometer, so that no thermometer wires and heating coils are required, and also that specific heats at liquid helium temperatures can be derived without the use of liquid helium.

4.3. Specific heats derived from magnetic measurements.

We have seen in the preceding section, that it is possible to determine the entropy of a substance by adiabatic demagnetization experiments in which the final field is zero. It is of some interest to point out, that by measurements of the magnetic moment in demagnetization experiments from a field H to a field $H - dH$, the specific heat in zero field may be determined. We will not assume that Curie's law holds, but only that no saturation effects occur so that the magnetic moment can be written as

$$M = \chi(T)H.$$

We have
$$S = S(0,T) + \tfrac{1}{2}\chi'H^2,$$

where we have put
$$\frac{d\chi}{dT} = \chi'.$$

Now during adiabatic experiments $dS = 0$, so that

$$0 = \frac{\partial S(0,T)}{\partial T}dT + \tfrac{1}{2}\chi''H^2 dT + \chi'H dH.$$

On the other hand $dM = \chi'H dT + \chi dH.$

Eliminating dT, we find

$$\left(\frac{\partial M}{\partial H}\right)_S = \chi(T)\frac{\partial S(0,T)/\partial T + (\tfrac{1}{2}\chi'' - \chi'^2/\chi)H^2}{\partial S(0,T)/\partial T + \tfrac{1}{2}\chi''H^2}. \tag{1}$$

Since
$$\frac{\partial S(0,T)}{\partial T} = \frac{C_p}{T},$$

this enables us to calculate C_p.

An important case is when χ follows the so-called Curie-Weiss law:

$$\chi = \frac{a}{T-\Theta};$$

in that case (1) reduces to

$$\left(\frac{\partial M}{\partial H}\right)_S = \frac{C_p}{C_p + \{aT/(T-\Theta)^3\}H^2}\chi(T). \qquad (2)$$

In 2.10 we have described how values of $\partial M/\partial H$ are easily obtained by the induction methods. If such measurements are carried out on a sample which is thermally insulated from the surrounding helium bath, they will give $(\partial M/\partial H)_S$. On the other hand $\chi(T)$ can be determined by measurements in zero external field when the sample is in thermal contact with the liquid helium. For reasons which will be explained in Chapter VII the determination of $(\partial M/\partial H)_S$ should be carried out by the ballistic method, and the thermal insulation has then to fulfil the condition that the time in which temperature equilibrium with the bath is restored is long compared with the period of the galvanometer.

We believe that (2) provides us with an accurate and very convenient method for determining the specific heat of paramagnetic salts in the liquid helium region.

4.4. Temperatures below 1° K.

Let us now consider the more interesting case in which temperatures well below 1° K. are obtained. The difficulty in interpreting the results is that the relation between susceptibility and temperature is not known.

The simplest type of experiment that can be carried out will now be described. A substance is magnetized at a temperature T in a field H. Then an adiabatic demagnetization is carried out. In the final state the magnetic moment is measured. The experiment shows, that a state in field H_2 and with magnetic moment M_2 has the same entropy as the initial state. One can introduce a provisional temperature scale by extrapolating

Curie's law. For temperatures above $1°$ K. we have for all suitable salts

$$M = \left(\frac{a}{T} + b\right) H,$$

provided H is not too large.

We now define the temperature T^* of the final state by putting

$$\frac{M_2}{H_2} = \frac{a}{T^*} + b. \tag{1}$$

Several remarks should be made in connection with this definition.

(*a*) The definition is only a reasonable extrapolation as long as M is very small compared with the saturation moment. If this is not the case it will be better to put

$$M = F\left(\frac{H}{T^*}\right),$$

where F is the function describing the magnetization at helium temperatures. For iron-ammonium alum H/T^* must be smaller than 1000 in order to obtain an accuracy of 1 %.

(*b*) The question arises whether one and the same body will have the same true thermodynamic temperature in states with identical T^* but different H. This depends on the question whether for fields below the limits specified under (*a*) the magnetic moment will be proportional to H. The answer to this question is not obvious; we will see later on, that at very low temperatures there will certainly exist exceptions. We will also see that there is good reason to believe that this proportionality will hold in a large region of fields and temperatures. But from a purely experimental point of view it is necessary to specify both T^* and H.

(*c*) For a given temperature T and a given exterior field H_0 the extrapolated temperature T^* will depend very strongly on the shape of the body, as was pointed out in the second chapter. Kürti and Simon [68] have proposed to reduce all measurements to the case of a sphere and much is to be said for such a convention. The necessary corrections to equation (1) are easily applied.

If a body with demagnetization coefficient α has a moment M in a field H_0 so that $T^* = aH_0/M$ (the constant b is assumed to be negligible), then the interior field is

$$H_i = H_0 - \alpha M/V.$$

In a sphere we would find this magnetization for the same interior field, that is for an exterior field

$$H_0{}^s = H_0 - \alpha M/V + \frac{4\pi}{3} M/V.$$

The extrapolated temperature would under these conditions be

$$T_s{}^* = \frac{aH_0{}^s}{M} = T^* + \left(\frac{4\pi}{3} - \alpha\right) a/V.$$

In view of the remark under (b) it should be remembered that not only the temperature but also the field should be corrected.

Of course we might also reduce all measurements to the case of an infinitely long sample, but we shall see in Chapter v that it is to be expected that for a sphere, the difference between T and T^* will be smaller than for any other case.

Strictly speaking one should expect that in the liquid helium region Curie's law holds only for the ratio M/H_0 for a sphere, and not for this ratio for any other shape of the salt. For an ellipsoid with demagnetization correction α, one should then find deviations from this law. Suppose that for a sphere

$$M/H_0 = a/T,$$

then for our spheroid

$$M/H_0 = a \bigg/ \left\{T - \left(\frac{4\pi}{3} - \alpha\right) a/V\right\} = a/(T - \Theta). \qquad (2)$$

For iron-ammonium alum and a spheroid with $c/a = 2$, $\Theta = 0.03°$ K., for an "infinitely" long sample $\Theta = 0.065°$ K. It is rather difficult to establish the existence of these corrections by measurements in the helium region, for if for temperatures between 4 and $1.2°$ K. the values of M/H_0 derived from (2) are plotted against $1/T$, the distance of these points from a straight line is only very small.

In practice the best way to reduce the observations to the case of a sphere is at once to plot the measured values of M/H_0 as a function of $1/(T - \Theta)$ with the theoretical value of Θ, and to draw a straight line through these points. Extrapolation of this line will then give T_S^* (cf. Kürti and Simon [68]).

Returning to the experiments described above, we can now say, that they show which values of T^* can be obtained under given experimental conditions. Since T and T^* will certainly be of the same order of magnitude, such experiments were sufficient to show the possibility of obtaining extremely low temperatures by the magnetic method. Further, if it is assumed, that the entropy in a magnetic field is correctly represented by the formulae of Chapter III, these experiments will also give the entropy as a function of T^*. The results can thus be compared with theoretical formulae if these give both the relation between T and T^* and the dependence of S on T. Finally these experiments make it possible to study the merits of various substances and also to predict qualitatively where Curie's law will break down. We have seen that Curie's law will hold as long as all the lowest levels are equally occupied, but if this is the case the entropy will be equal to $Nk^e\log n$ (where n is the number of levels). No large deviations from Curie's law are to be expected as long as the entropy does not appreciably differ from this value. For iron-ammonium alum for instance, a field of 2000 G. at $1°$ K. will lead to a decrease of entropy of 18×10^{-4} watt sec./degree per gram, whereas $Nk^e\log 6$ corresponds to roughly 24×10^{-3} watt sec./degree per gram. The entropy is thus diminished by only 10 % and Curie's law will hold approximately. The lower the temperatures which are reached by a field not producing saturation, the further down Curie's law will hold. Of course these arguments are only qualitative. A more quantitative discussion must be postponed to the following chapters.

4.5. Measurements in intermediate fields.

By extending the measurements to fields intermediate between the final and initial field we can obtain M as a function of H at constant entropy. From such isentropic curves in the M, H-diagram a number of important quantities can be derived.

First of all we can find the internal energy U at any point of the M, H-diagram provided the energy in the initial state is known. For, since no heat is supplied, the change of internal energy must be equal to the work done by the exterior field. Since

$$dQ = dU - H\,dM \quad \text{and} \quad dQ = 0,$$

we have along an isentropic curve, starting at H_1 and a temperature T_1,

$$U(H) = U(H_1) - \int_H^{H_1} H\,dM,$$

or

$$U - HM = \{U(H_1) - H_1 M\} + \int_H^{H_1} M\,dH.$$

As was seen in 2.11 $U(H_1)$ can be calculated when $U(H = 0, T_1)$ and $M(H,T)$ in the neighbourhood of $T = T_1$ are known.

There are now various methods to arrive at an expression for the thermodynamic scale. In the first place we have, since

$$T\,dS = \left(\frac{\partial U}{\partial S} - H\frac{\partial M}{\partial S}\right) dS,$$

$$T = \frac{\partial}{\partial S}(U - HM),$$

and hence

$$T = T_1 + \int_H^{H_1} \left(\frac{\partial M}{\partial S}\right)_H dH.$$

This equation enables us to calculate the temperature when the $M(H)_S$ curve for two neighbouring states is known. This procedure for determining the absolute temperature has been put forward by Giauque and MacDougall [18, 19].

De Haas and Wiersma [45] have called special attention to the case when M remains constant during the demagnetization process. In that case

$$T = T_1 - A(H_1 - H),$$

or, putting

$$A = \frac{T_1 + B}{H_1},$$

$$T = T_1 - \frac{T_1 + B}{H_1}(H_1 - H),$$

whence

$$H/(T + B) = H_1/(T_1 + B). \tag{1}$$

If the magnetic moment remains constant during adiabatic de-magnetization, then we can write

$$M = f\left(\frac{H}{T+B}\right),$$

and also

$$M = f\left(\frac{H-C}{T}\right),$$

where B and C are functions of M. The constants B and C can in principle be determined by very accurate measurements of magnetization curves in the ordinary liquid helium region.

A second possibility is to derive the energy as a function of the final slope of the M, H-curve, that is, as a function of T^*. We can find the function $U(H = 0, T^*)$ from magnetic measurements. The specific heat in terms of T^* can be derived by differentiation. For the thermodynamic temperature T it follows

$$T = \frac{\partial U/\partial T^*}{\partial S/\partial T^*}. \qquad (2)$$

It would thus appear, that measurements of isentropic M, H-curves and of magnetization curves at known helium temperatures, is all that is required for obtaining complete diagrams for entropy, internal energy and magnetic moment as a function of H and of the true temperature. However, a closer investigation shows that in order to obtain in this way the thermodynamic scale with a moderate degree of accuracy extremely accurate magnetic measurements would be necessary. This applies to the second procedure as well as to the first one, and also to the special case of de Haas and Wiersma.

This does not mean that measurements of this type are without interest. The results can for instance be compared with theoretical formulae. Further, certain qualitative features of M, H-curves are of interest. These curves are such that M remains fairly constant down to a field H_k, which is more or less independent of the initial conditions, and then decreases rapidly to zero. This field H_k is a very characteristic quantity for a paramagnetic substance.

Finally, although the method cannot be expected to give accurate values for $\partial U(0, T^*)/\partial T^*$, it will give the value of $U(0, T^*)$ with fair accuracy.

4.6. Caloric measurements.

Instead of deriving the quantity $\partial U/\partial T^*$ from magnetic measurements it can also be found by straightforward calorimetric determination: one has to measure the quantity of heat necessary to raise the temperature from T^* to $T^* + dT^*$. Also the entropy in the initial state might be found by direct measurements, but of course it remains necessary to determine the initial states corresponding to T^* and $T^* + dT^*$. The procedure for determining T, which is expressed by equation 4.5 (2) can now be formulated as follows. Suppose that the state H_1, T_1 corresponds to T^* and the state $H_1 - dH_1, T_1$ to $T^* + dT^*$; let dQ_1 be the heat developed when the salt is brought from $H_1 - dH_1, T_1$ to H_1, T_1 and dQ_2 the heat required to heat the salt from T^* to $T^* + dT^*$, then

$$\frac{dQ_1}{dQ_2} = \frac{T_1}{T^*}.$$

This formulation, which is a direct application of Carnot's principle, is due to Keesom.

It will be seen that the method depends on the determination of the quotients dU/dT^*, dT^*/dH_1, and dQ_1/dH_1. The accuracy of the determination of T depends on the accuracy with which each of these quantities can be determined. In the determination of dT^*/dH_1, it is necessary to assume that the process takes place at constant entropy. Whether this will be the case depends on the thermal insulation and also on the question whether the salt passes through equilibrium states.

Of course the calorimetric measurements are not only of interest in view of a determination of the temperature. From a theoretical point of view also the specific heats themselves are of considerable importance.

4.7. Combination of magnetic and caloric measurements.

The procedure of de Haas and Wiersma has several disadvantages: it can only be applied for magnetic fields above a certain limit, it is difficult to obtain a sufficient degree of accuracy and it contains a constant B which can hardly be determined at all. On the other hand it follows from theoretical considerations, that whenever the moment remains fairly constant down to a field H_c one must expect that the variation down to a field of say $5H_c$ will be extremely small. For CsTi alum we can, for example, safely apply the equation

$$T + B = \frac{H}{H_1}(T_1 + B) \qquad (1)$$

down to 500 G. when H_1/T_1 is of the order of 20,000.

The situation becomes much more satisfactory when the method is combined with caloric measurements. Indeed, by such measurements one can find the ratio between temperatures in different fields and it will be possible to test equation (1) and also to determine the constant B. When it is found that (1) holds in fields between for instance 500 and 2000 G. it will certainly hold between 500 G. and the high initial field. The method of de Haas and Wiersma can then be used to fix the factor, still left indeterminate by the caloric measurements; also by extending the caloric measurements down to zero fields the relation between T^* and T will be found.

4.8. Cooling of other substances by paramagnetic salts.

We will now discuss experiments in which a paramagnetic salt is used to cool other substances. The investigation of properties of matter at those very low temperatures is hardly started. We will here consider only the thermodynamic side of the question. Let us suppose that starting from initial conditions H_0, T_0 a final temperature T^* is reached. If we start with initial conditions H_1, T_0 we have the entropy $S(H_0, T_0) - S(H_1, T_0)$ at our disposal to cool other substances. Now for iron-ammonium alum a field of a few thousand Gauss at $1°$ K. is sufficient to reach a T^* of $0·2°$ K. Thus nearly the whole entropy $R^e \log 6$ can be made available for cooling purposes. This is enormous compared with the specific heats of non-magnetic substances. A crystal like KCl for example has a specific heat of $8·6 \times 10^{-6} T^3$ watt sec./degree per c.c. in the liquid helium region and there is every reason to believe that no appreciable deviations will occur at still lower temperatures. For the entropy difference between 1 and 0° K. we find, therefore, $\frac{1}{3} \times 8\cdot6 \times 10^{-6}$ watt sec. per c.c. This means that one ounce of iron-ammonium alum would be sufficient to cool 10 cubic feet of KCl. The only non-magnetic substance with a specific heat comparable to that of a paramagnetic salt is liquid helium.

4.9. Survey of experimental methods.

De Haas and Wiersma's first experiments were carried out by the balance method. The main difficulty was to obtain thermal insulation after demagnetization. This problem was solved by mounting the sample in a tube, containing helium gas at very low pressure. When the salt is cooled by demagnetization this gas is adsorbed and a certain degree of insulation is obtained. Very small quantities of salt were sufficient and though the thermal insulation was usually not very good, the heating rate was sufficiently slow to allow measurements of magnetization in the final field, which was of the order of a few hundred Gauss. Apart from the special sample tube no apparatus was required beside the usual set up for balance measurements. In this way a rapid survey of a large number of substances was made. The research was started on salts of the rare earths, but it was found in the course of the work, that for the purpose of obtaining very low temperatures the salts of the iron group are much more suitable. These results were very important in that they confirmed the expectation that adiabatic demagnetization offers a comparatively easy way of approach to temperatures far below 1° K. Perhaps it is unfortunate that no more attention was given to the determination of magnetic moments in intermediate fields, for the method would have been admirably suitable for that purpose.

In all other measurements the susceptibility was measured by an induction method, either with a ballistic galvanometer (de Haas and Wiersma, Kürti and Simon) or with A.C. (Giauque). The field may be produced by a big coil (Giauque) or a magnet (de Haas and Wiersma, Kürti and Simon). In the first case the

Dewar vessel and the coil can remain in place during the measurements but in the second case it is necessary to provide arrangements for either removing the magnet—which is of course only feasible for very small magnets—or removing the Dewar vessel with the liquid helium and the salt. The difficulty of this last process is, that a vacuum line and a pumping line must be attached to the helium vessel. So one must either work with ground joints (de Haas and Wiersma) or move the pumps with the apparatus (Simon).

It would appear that the use of fairly small high powered water cooled coils—with or without iron—such as have been constructed by Bitter and by Ashmead in the Mond Laboratory, will greatly facilitate the technique. The mounting of the specimen was essentially the same in all three cases. Fig. 7 shows a sample tube used in the Leiden Laboratory. Thermal equilibrium with the liquid helium is established by helium gas at low pressure; after magnetization the tube is evacuated. Thermal insulation can be made extremely good. First of all the heat conductivity becomes very small at low temperatures, radiation may be practically eliminated and finally any traces of helium still present in the tube will presumably be adsorbed on the salt so that a very perfect vacuum is obtained.

Fig. 7. Sample tube: *a*, spheroid of glass filled with powder; *b*, thin-walled support.

Still it should be mentioned here, that notwithstanding these ideal circumstances difficulties will often arise. In many measurements even a small heat leak will be very disturbing, especially since in general it will tend to cause an inhomogeneous temperature distribution inside the salt.

4.9[1]. Measurements in intermediate fields.

The experimental methods for such measurements have been discussed at length in the first chapter. Extensive measurements of this type were made by Giauque and MacDougall [20], using the $\partial M/\partial H$ method. Some of the results of de Haas and Wiersma, obtained by using the ballistic method with fairly high measuring fields may also be mentioned here.

Some of the results will be discussed in Chapter VI.

4.9². Caloric measurements.

Here a new technique is required. It is necessary to supply a known amount of heat to the salt. In principle there is a large number of possibilities, but all of them involve certain disadvantages. First of all one may use a heating coil of known resistance through which a known current is passing; this is the usual method in low temperature calorimetry, and an advantage is that the quantity of heat can be very accurately measured. The necessary leads give rise to a technical complication but they do not lead to serious difficulties. They do not have a serious effect on the warming up rate, when they are sufficiently long and thin and the best procedure is probably to use lead wires of impure lead (de Haas, Casimir and v. d. Berg [46]) for, since lead is superconductive, no heat is developed in the leads, whereas the thermal resistance is high. The main disadvantage is that one does not know whether the coil is in equilibrium with the salt, and whether there is temperature equilibrium in the salt itself. Even if after each heating period an apparent state of equilibrium is reached in a few minutes or so, this does not always mean that in this state the temperature is really homogeneous; a striking example is given by the results of de Haas, Casimir and v. d. Berg. The influence of a lack of equilibrium is especially disastrous since the magnetic measurements will give an average of $1/T$. Although the procedure will probably work satisfactorily at temperatures only a few tenths of a degree below $1°$ K. (some preliminary results were published by Clark in his thesis [7]) it seems very diffficult to obtain in this way reliable results at very low temperatures.

Giauque has used an induction heater. This enables one to avoid leads, but one has to assume that the resistance remains constant, and further, either place the ring in which an alternating current is induced far outside the salt, or correct for the influence of the salt on the number of lines of force passing through the ring. The difficulties as regards temperature equilibrium are the same as in the preceding case.

Kürti, Lainé and Simon (66) have used a completely different procedure. They supply heat by means of radioactive substances. There are two possibilities: either the substance is mixed with a substance emitting α-rays, e.g. polonium, or the salt is irradiated with γ-rays. In the first case the total amount of heat is known. In the second case a determination of the total energy adsorbed

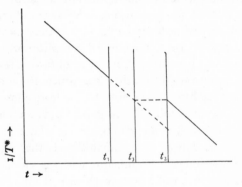

Fig. 8.

would be rather difficult. The specific heat $\partial U/\partial T^*$ will thus contain an undetermined constant factor. It can be found by postulating that the thermodynamic temperature derived from the determination of $\partial U/\partial T^*$ agrees with T^* for "high" temperatures. So far only preliminary notes have appeared.

Recently Kürti and Simon (67) have reported on some preliminary experiments on the determination of the ratio between temperatures in external fields. They have pointed out that such experiments are very easy to perform, since it is not necessary to make any measurements at all, in the intermediate fields. This is best explained by considering fig. 8. The curve represents the change of T^* (in a low measuring field) due to heating with γ-rays as a function of time. At the moment t_1 a field H_c is switched on and the measurement is stopped. At the moment t_2 the field is switched off and the measurement of T^* is resumed. Now the curve for $t > t_2$ will not be the continuation of the curve for $t < t_1$. The change of entropy during the time $t_2 - t_1$ in the field H_c, is equal to the change which would take place in zero field during the time $t_3 - t_1$. Since the heat supplied per second is equal in both cases it follows that

$$T_H/T_{H=0} = (t_2 - t_1)/(t_3 - t_1).$$

It has been explained in 4.7 how such measurements will make it possible to determine the absolute temperature. Of all available methods this procedure will probably give the most reliable results, since it seems to be free of any of the drawbacks of other procedures. Even the existence of a heat leak not entirely negligible compared with the influence of the γ-rays would not do much harm.

A difficulty specially emphasized by Giauque and MacDougall is that even if the heat is applied homogeneously, the heat leak will in the first place warm the surface of the sample. Thus the warming up curves will be reliable immediately after demagnetization, but when the measurements are carried on for a long time the temperature distribution will become more and more inhomogeneous, at least when the heat conductivity of the sample is low.

The published data show, certainly, that a determination of the thermodynamic temperature is possible, but also that it is very difficult to obtain a reasonable degree of precision.

4.10. Ferromagnetism.

A new feature was introduced into the study of purely magnetic properties by the discovery of Simon, Kürti and collaborators [64] that paramagnetic substances show at very low temperatures a behaviour which may be described as "ferromagnetism", although much more work will be required before we can decide whether there is no fundamental difference with true ferro-magnetism. The most remarkable point is the existence of hysteresis. This occurs below a certain temperature (Curie temperature). In the neighbourhood of the Curie point there is an enormous increase of specific heat and near this temperature the difference between T and T^* is very marked.

Very little is known about the details of magnetization curves. We do not know whether the hysteresis depends on the constitution of the salt, there exist very few data concerning the dependence on the field, and so on.

It was suggested by de Haas and the author that the existence of hysteresis might be used for calorimetric purposes. For if an alternating field is applied an amount of heat proportional to the surface of the hysteresis loop is supplied during each period of the field. On the other hand the surface of this loop can be determined by means of a bridge method.

The existence of ferromagnetism will cause a dependence of T^* on the measuring field, so that great care must be taken when defining T^*.

4.11. Summary of thermodynamic properties.

We will briefly summarize the situation. The magnetic and thermodynamic properties of a paramagnetic substance will be completely known when we know the magnetic moment, the interior energy and the entropy as a function of H and T. The difference with the analogous problem in the case of gases, is that the substance itself must be used for obtaining the low temperatures, and that the temperature cannot be measured directly but must be derived from other measured quantities. Therefore it is useful first to introduce H and M as independent variables and to define a temperature T^* by extrapolating Curie's law. By adiabatic demagnetization experiments it is possible to find points on isentropic curves in the M, H-diagram, and if we assume that the entropy in the initial state is known, we can obtain the entropy as a function of M and H. Our problem will be completely solved when we also know the energy as a function of M and H, since the relation between T and T^* can then be found by thermodynamics. In principle the energy can be derived from magnetic measurements, but it is difficult to obtain sufficient accuracy and it is better to use caloric measurements. Probably the best procedure for obtaining T as a function of T^* is to combine the magnetic and the caloric method.

Chapter V

THEORETICAL DISCUSSION OF PARAMAGNETISM AT VERY LOW TEMPERATURES

5.1. Statement of problem.

The object of a theoretical study of paramagnetic salts at very low temperatures, must be to calculate the energy, entropy and susceptibility as a function of temperature and of the external field. In Chapter III this problem was solved for the region of temperature where Curie's law is valid; we will now have to investigate the deviations from Curie's law and the behaviour of the specific heat when T approaches to zero. The splittings and broadenings of levels, which are of no importance at high temperatures, are now essential and will have to be studied in detail. There are two reasons for these splittings: partly they are due to the influence of the electric field of surrounding atoms, and partly to the influence of interaction between magnetic ions. The first factor is in one respect the most simple: it leaves the problem a one atom problem. We can study by well-known methods the influence of a given electric field on the levels of a magnetic ion, and the properties of a crystal can then be calculated by the methods of Chapter III. On the other hand, the electric field is unknown and at present it seems hardly feasible to calculate it with any degree of accuracy from the crystal structure of the substance. At most we can predict the symmetry of the field and we are left with a field containing one or two arbitrary constants. In the case of magnetic interaction the situation is rather the other way round: the expression for the interaction is well known and so is the distance between magnetic ions. But the many atom problem encountered here, offers great mathematical difficulties and until now it has been necessary either to restrict oneself to certain approximations, or to use certain hypotheses which cannot be rigorously justified. The situation is very analogous to that encountered in the theory of the equation of state of gases, where one must either restrict oneself to a calculation of the second virial coefficient or otherwise use an equation like that of van der Waals which is strictly speaking a completely unallowed extrapolation. Only in the magnetic case the interaction is known and so perhaps a rigorous solution might be possible. A further complication, however, is introduced by the possibility that besides magnetic interaction there may also exist exchange coupling.

5.2. Electric fields and Kramers' theorem.

We will only discuss ions with an odd number of electrons. Now there exists a theorem of Kramers [51], stating that, whatever electric fields are applied, all states of such ions remain at least twofold degenerate. For a proof we refer to the original paper.

5.2¹. The case of one spin; titanium.

The best known example is the Ti ion; although we shall see in the next chapter that more experimental data are badly wanted. The free ion is in a ^{2}D-state; there is only one d-electron outside a closed shell. Probably in a crystal the ion behaves as if there were only one spin. This means that the D-state is split by the crystalline field in such a way, that the lowest state is non-degenerate, as far as the orbit is concerned (quenching of orbital magnetism); the distance to the next level must certainly be very much larger than $k.20°$ K. The lowest level is now doubly degenerate because of the spin, and according to Kramers' theorem, the electric field will have no influence on this degeneracy. It does not follow from Kramers' theorem, that the magnetic moment of this double state is necessarily one Bohr magneton. This depends on the distance to the next higher level.

5.2². Three spins; the chromium ion.

The fundamental state of the chromium ion is a ^{4}F-state; there are three d-electrons with their spins parallel. The susceptibility of potassium-chromium alum and probably of many other salts is such as if there were only three free spins. This means again that the F-state is split by the electric field, in such a way that the lowest state is non-degenerate apart from the spin degeneracy. According to Kramers this fourfold degenerate state can be split into two twofold degenerate states by an electric field. However, in a field of cubic symmetry no such splitting will occur, the reason being that the four wave-functions transform with an irreducible representation of the cubic group. In a trigonal field, however, splitting will occur. The two states with angular momentum $+3/2$ and $-3/2$ in the direction of the trigonal axis, will be separated from the two states with angular momentum $+1/2$ and $-1/2$. The situation is thus completely described by one parameter, giving the distance between the $1/2$, $-1/2$ and the $3/2$, $-3/2$ levels.

It is interesting that these conclusions can be reached without considering the mechanism which leads to the splitting. This is rather complicated. On the one hand there is a spin orbit inter-action, which to a first approximation has no influence on the levels, and on the other hand there is an influence of the electric fields on the orbital wave-functions. The combined action of these two factors will in higher approximation lead to a splitting.

We can at once write down the thermodynamic functions. Let δ be the distance between the two groups of levels, then the partition function is given by

$$Z = 2(1 + e^{-\delta/kT}).$$

It follows, that

$$E = \frac{2\delta N e^{-\delta/kT}}{2(1 + e^{-\delta/kT})},$$

and the specific heat is given by

$$C = \frac{\delta^2}{4k^2T^2}(Nk)\frac{4e^{-\delta/kT}}{(1 + e^{-\delta/kT})^2}.$$

The entropy decreases with decreasing temperature from $Nk\,{}^e\!\log 4$ to $Nk\,{}^e\!\log 2$ and is given by

$$S = Nk\left[{}^e\!\log 2(1 + e^{-\delta/kT}) + \frac{\delta}{kT}\frac{e^{-\delta/kT}}{1 + e^{-\delta/kT}}\right].$$

The susceptibility will depend on the orientation of the external field with respect to the trigonal axis. We will give only the formula for the average over all orientations which holds when the $\frac{3}{2}$, $-\frac{3}{2}$ level is lowest,

$$\chi = \frac{4\mu_B{}^2 N}{3kT} \cdot \frac{3}{2} \cdot \frac{5}{2} \cdot \frac{2}{5Z}\left[(3+4kT/\delta)+(3-4kT/\delta)e^{-\delta/kT}\right].$$

It is easy to derive expressions for the thermodynamic functions in an arbitrarily large magnetic field; in the following no such formulae will be required.

5.2³. The mechanism of "quenching".

In the preceding sections, we have simply assumed that the influence of the crystalline fields on the orbital wave-function, is such that there is a lowest state, non-degenerate apart from spin degeneracy and with a fairly large distance from the next level. For our purpose it is not necessary to know exactly how this comes about, but the question is of considerable theoretical importance. The subject has been investigated by Siegert (74, 75), but the situation has not been made completely clear.

5.2⁴. Five spins; the iron ion.

Here the ion is in a ⁶S-state. In first approximation an electric field has no influence on such a state and it is easy to understand, that the magnetic moment is correctly described by the "spin only" value. But in higher approximation there does exist an influence of the electric fields, which causes a small splitting. According to Kramers' theorem the sixfold degenerate level might be separated into three doubly degenerate levels and the partition function would then contain two parameters, δ_1 and δ_2, being the distances of two levels from the lowest level. We will only write down the first term of a series development of C obtaining in that case:

$$C = Nk \cdot \frac{2}{9} \cdot \frac{\delta_1{}^2 + \delta_2{}^2 - \delta_1 \delta_2}{(kT)^2} + O\left(\frac{\delta}{kT}\right)^3 + \dots.$$

One can show that in a cubic field the sixfold degenerate level will separate into one fourfold degenerate level and one doubly degenerate level. In that case the formulae will be considerably simplified. We are inclined to believe, however, that it will not be possible to obtain a satisfactory description of the behaviour of iron salts, and especially of iron-ammonium alum, by assuming cubic symmetry. The formulae holding in that case can be found in the paper of Hebb and Purcell, and we will not repeat them here. It might be of some importance to study theoretically the combined action of a cubic and a trigonal field on the iron ion.

5.2⁵. Seven spins; gadolinium.

The ion is here in an ^{8}S-state. The situation is very analogous to that in the case of iron, but slightly more complicated. In a cubic field the eightfold degenerate state is split into two doubly degenerate levels and one fourfold degenerate level which is between the two others the spacing being in the ratio 3 : 5. Again we shall not write down the formulae for entropy, specific heat and susceptibility which were derived by Hebb and Purcell for this case, and only remark that the first term in the series development of C is given by

$$C = Nk \frac{1}{(kT)^2} \left[\frac{1}{4} \sum_{i=1}^{3} \delta_i^2 - \frac{1}{16} \left(\sum_{i=1}^{3} \delta_i \right)^2 \right],$$

where δ_i are the distances to the lowest level. In the case of a cubic field this reduces to:

$$C = Nk \left(\frac{\Delta}{kT} \right)^2 \cdot \frac{33}{256},$$

where Δ is the overall splitting.

5.3. Magnetic interaction.

5.3¹. The Lorentz field.

The simplest way of describing the magnetic interaction between ions is to use the so-called Lorentz field. It is assumed that each ion can be treated as an ion in a constant field, which is equal to the external field plus the field corresponding to the average magnetic moment of all the other ions. The calculation of this second term can now be simplified by dividing all the magnetic ions into two groups: those outside a sphere with its centre in the atom and those inside this sphere. The radius of this sphere is chosen so large, that outside this sphere the crystal can be treated as a continuum. The field inside the sphere caused by a homogeneous magnetization J outside the sphere will then be given by

$$H_i = H + \frac{4\pi}{3} J = H_0 + \left(\frac{4\pi}{3} - \alpha\right) J. \qquad (1)$$

The field H_i is equal to the exterior field plus the field of "magnetic charges" on the outer surface of the body, being $-\alpha J$, and the field of magnetic charges on the surface of this sphere, being $(4\pi/3) J$. The contribution of the ions inside the sphere can be calculated by straightforward summation, but in many cases it can be seen to be zero by reasons of symmetry. Equation (1) gives then the correct expression for the interior field. For a sphere the interior field is equal to the exterior field. And all other cases can be reduced to this case by applying demagnetization corrections.

It is very important to remark that in this calculation one does not really "take away" part of the crystal or consider what is happening in a cavity in the crystal—as is sometimes erroneously stated. The introduction of the spherical surface is only a mathematical artifice by which a sum over all ions is reduced to an easily calculated integral and a sum over the ions inside a sphere.

It will be seen that the deduction does not assume that the magnetism is due to free ions; it will hold just as well when the ions are influenced by electric fields.

If we combine the considerations of 2.3 with the results of this section we find that the total correction is now given by

$$H_0 - H_i = \left[f\alpha_e + (1-f)\frac{4\pi}{3} - \frac{4\pi}{3} \right] J = f\left(\alpha_e - \frac{4\pi}{3}\right) J.$$

When the density is changed in the ratio $1 : f$ the total field due to the magnetic ions must be changed in this same ratio.

5.3². Onsager's theory.

A somewhat closer investigation shows at once that a theory of the type described above can never be rigorous. Until recently, however, little attention has been paid to this fact; this was partly due to the circumstance that one failed to distinguish between the case of polarization of atoms—in which case Lorentz's formula is exact—and the case of orientation. Onsager[73] has drawn attention to this point and also shown in which way one may expect to find a better approximation. It is certainly true that the average field caused by the ions inside the spherical surface in Lorentz's theory is zero, but it is *not* this average field in which we are interested, for in calculating the average we have also taken the average over all orientations of the moment of the ion considered. But what we really want to know, is the field caused by the surrounding ions for one given orientation of this moment. This field will be equal to a field H_{np} which would be there if the ion were not present at all, and an induced field H_{in}. This induced field will change its direction with the dipole—we assume that the neighbourhood of this ion is isotropic—and will therefore not lead to an orientation of the magnetic dipole (although it does lead to an energy). The field H_{np} together with the average value of the induced field will be equal to the Lorentz field, but if we want to calculate the orientation of each ion, we have to take H_{np}. The problem is now to calculate the average moment of all ions inside a spherical surface, when one ion in the centre is missing, and to find the corresponding value of the field in the centre of the sphere. It is rather difficult to do this by an exact calculation, but to obtain an approximation, Onsager replaces all ions by a continuum, and the absence of one ion is described by making in this continuum a spherical cavity of a properly chosen radius. It will be clear that this way of introducing a spherical surface is fundamentally different from the procedure used in the Lorentz theory. Here we really introduce a spherical cavity as a schematic *model*. The calculation is now carried out by means of well-known formulae of magnetostatics. The field inside a spherical cavity in a medium with permeability μ is given by

$$H_i = \frac{3\mu}{2\mu + 1} H = \left[1 + \frac{\mu - 1}{2\mu + 1} \right] H, \qquad (1)$$

where H is connected with the exterior field H_0 by the ordinary demagnetization corrections. According to Onsager's theory the inner field working on each ion is given by equation (1). To a first approximation in $\mu - 1$ this field agrees with the Lorentz field

$$H_i = \left[1 + \frac{\mu - 1}{3} \right] H.$$

We shall now calculate the susceptibilities. Let χ be the susceptibility, i.e. the ratio between M and H_0 for an infinitely long specimen, and χ_0 the susceptibility which one would find for independent ions.

We have $\qquad \chi = \chi_0 H_i / H.$

The Lorentz formula gives

$$\chi = \chi_0 \left[1 + \frac{4\pi}{3} \chi \right],$$

and hence

$$\chi = \frac{\chi_0}{1 - \dfrac{4\pi}{3} \chi_0}.$$

The Onsager formula is

$$\chi = \chi_0 \left[1 + \frac{4\pi\chi}{3 + 8\pi\chi} \right],$$

and the solution is

$$\chi = \chi_0 \left\{ \frac{3}{4} - \frac{3}{16\pi\chi_0} + \left(\frac{9}{16} + \frac{3}{32\pi\chi_0} + \frac{9}{256\pi^2\chi_0^2} \right)^{\frac{1}{2}} \right\}.$$

For a spheroid with demagnetization factor α, we have

$$\frac{M}{H_0} = \frac{\chi}{1 + \alpha\chi}.$$

If we assume the Lorentz formula, this reduces to

$$\frac{M}{H_0} = \frac{\chi_0}{1 - \left(\dfrac{4\pi}{3} - \alpha \right) \chi_0};$$

in the Onsager theory there results a more complicated expression. The first terms of a power series development are in the Lorentz theory

$$\frac{M}{H_0} = \chi_0 \left[1 + \left(\frac{4\pi}{3} - \alpha \right) \chi_0 + \left(\frac{4\pi}{3} - \alpha \right)^2 \chi_0^2 + \dots \right];$$

and, in the Onsager theory,

$$\frac{M}{H_0} = \chi_0 \left[1 + \left(\frac{4\pi}{3} - \alpha \right) \chi_0 + \left(\frac{4\pi}{3} - \alpha \right)^2 \chi_0^2 - \frac{2}{9} (4\pi\chi_0)^2 \ldots \right].$$

To give an idea of the order of magnitude of the difference between the two formulae we mention that for iron-ammonium alum at one degree $\frac{2}{9}(4\pi\chi_0)^2 = 0.84 \times 10^{-2}$. At $0.2°$ K. it would amount to 0.21.

Onsager's analysis establishes beyond doubt that deviations from the Lorentz formula of the order of magnitude $(4\pi\chi_0/3)^2$ will occur. On the other hand, since the geometric arrangement of molecules is described by a rather crude model, it is not to be expected, that this correction term will appear with the correct numerical factor.

Even apart from this circumstance Onsager's deduction will give only a second approximation; it can hardly be assumed, that a simple "interior field" theory of this type will lead to a rigorous solution of the magnetic interaction problem. All these facts will be borne out more clearly by the rigorous theory discussed in later sections.

5.4. Magnetic specific heat.

We have seen that in Onsager's theory the field H_{in}, induced by one ion in the surrounding distribution of ions, does not contribute to the susceptibility. However, it will give rise to a magnetic interaction energy. If R is the radius of the cavity surrounding one ion, then the field induced by a moment m placed in the centre of this cavity, will be

$$H_{in} = \frac{2(\mu - 1)}{2\mu + 1} \frac{1}{R^3} m,$$

and this will cause a potential energy

$$\Delta V = - \frac{\mu - 1}{2\mu + 1} \frac{1}{R^3} m^2.$$

We shall not dwell upon the arguments necessary to derive from this expression the equation for the free energy and the specific heat, and only mention the result for the case when Curie's law is strictly valid and $(\mu - 1) = 4\pi m^2/3kT$. In that case the specific heat per c.c. will be given by

$$C_m = \frac{1}{R^3} N \frac{4\pi}{9} m^4 \cdot \frac{1}{T^2}$$

if N is the number of atoms per c.c. Now it is reasonable to put $(4\pi/3) R^3 N = 1$ so that

$$C_m = \frac{16\pi^2}{27} N^2 m^4 \cdot \frac{1}{T^2}.$$

We shall not discuss this equation quantitatively, since it is to be expected that the numerical factors will be modified by a more rigorous calculation. But we draw attention to certain qualitative features, which hold just as well in a more rigorous theory: the fact that each magnetic ion has a tendency to cause an orientation of its neighbour leads to an additional specific heat. This specific heat is proportional to $1/T^2$, varies as the square of the number of ions/c.c. and as the fourth power of the magnetic moment.

5.4¹. The $1/T^2$ law.

It follows from the foregoing considerations, that both the Stark effect and the magnetic interaction lead to a specific heat of the form A/T^2 and, provided that the Stark splitting and the magnetic interaction are not too large, there will always be a region where the specific heat is given by

$$C_p = A/T^2 + BT^3.$$

In this region the susceptibility will be given with a fair degree of accuracy by

$$\chi = a/(T - \Theta).$$

In this region one can then easily calculate the result of adiabatic demagnetization experiments and the isentropic M, H-curves. We would like to draw special attention to the remarkably simple results which are obtained when BT^3 and Θ are neglected. For an adiabatic demagnetization process we have

$$0 = \frac{A}{T^2} dT - H dM.$$

On the other hand

$$dM = -\frac{aH}{T^2}dT + \frac{a}{T}dH = -\frac{aH^2}{A}dM + \frac{a}{T}dH,$$

and hence

$$\left(\frac{dM}{dH}\right)_{ad} = \frac{a}{T} \cdot \frac{1}{1 + aH^2/A}.$$

The ratio of the adiabatic and the isothermal dM/dH will thus be seen to be independent of temperature. Further we have

$$\frac{A}{T^2}dT = -\frac{aH^2}{T^2}dT + \frac{aH}{T}dH,$$

$$\frac{dT}{T} = \frac{aH}{A + aH^2}dH;$$

so that

$$\frac{T}{T_0} = \sqrt{\frac{A + aH^2}{A + aH_0^2}}, \qquad (1)$$

and

$$\frac{M}{M_0} = \frac{H}{H_0}\sqrt{\frac{A + aH_0^2}{A + aH^2}}. \qquad (2)$$

It is true that at $1°$ K. the lattice specific heat will often not be entirely negligible compared with the term A/T^2. But since the ratio varies as T^5, at 0.5 degree this condition will usually be fulfilled and from there on the M, H-curve should be given by (2). Thus under suitable conditions there may exist a temperature region where (1) and (2) obtain, and in this region the shape of the adiabatic M, H-curves does not depend on the initial conditions. It should thus be possible to determine a/A with high accuracy by measuring a few points on such curves.

5.5. Van Vleck's method.

Waller [81], and in greater detail, Van Vleck [78], have developed a general method for calculating magnetic interactions. Their procedure consists in developing the partition function in a series of ascending powers of $1/T$ and is somewhat analogous to the method used in the theory of the equation of state for calculating virial coefficients.

If for each of the N ions in a cubic centimetre we take into account n states, the Hamiltonian is a matrix of n^N rows and columns, and the representation of this matrix is known in a system of wave-functions, corresponding to the case when interaction is neglected. Now instead of determining the energy levels corresponding to this matrix and calculating

$$Z = \sum_{i=1}^{n^N} e^{-E_i/kT},$$

we may also write

$$Z = S[e^{-\mathscr{H}/kT}],$$

where $\mathscr{H}$ is the Hamiltonian matrix and S the diagonal sum of the matrix in square brackets. But since this diagonal sum does not depend on the system of wave-functions it can be calculated in the original representation. We can now expand Z in a power series

$$Z = S\left[1 - \frac{\mathscr{H}}{kT} + \frac{1}{2}\frac{\mathscr{H}^2}{(kT)^2} - \cdots \right],$$

and hence

$$Z = n^N - \frac{1}{kT}S(\mathscr{H}) + \frac{1}{2(kT)^2}S(\mathscr{H}^2) + \cdots.$$

The problem is thus reduced to the calculation of the diagonal sum of powers of the Hamiltonian. Such calculations are usually comparatively simple for the first and second power but become extremely cumbersome for higher powers. The susceptibility as a function of temperature can be derived from the expression for Z when the term $-H\mu$ is included in the Hamiltonian.

5.5¹. Specific heat; no Stark splitting.

If there are no Stark splittings, the Hamiltonian in zero external field will be given by

$$\mathscr{H} = \sum_{i>k} W_{ik},$$

where W_{ik} is the expression for the interaction between two magnetic ions. If only magnetic interaction is taken into account, we have

$$W_{ik} = \left[\frac{\mu_i \mu_k}{r_{ik}^3} - \frac{3(\mu_i r_{ik})(\mu_k r_{ik})}{r_{ik}^5} \right],$$

where μ_i, μ_k are the magnetic moment matrices.

However, there may also exist an exchange coupling between ions. We will not consider in detail these exchange terms and only mention that in most cases of practical importance they can be written in the form

$$w_{ik}\mu_i\mu_k,$$

where w_{ik} is a scalar quantity proportional to the exchange integral between the ions.

It is now easily proved that

$$S(\mathscr{H}) = 0.$$

To write down the next approximation it is useful to introduce a parameter τ defined by

$$\tau = g^2\mu_B{}^2NJ(J+1)/k.$$

Here J is the quantum number, μ_B the Bohr magneton, g the g-factor and hence $gJ\mu_B$ is the total magnetic moment; N is, as before, the number of atoms per c.c. One finds

$$Z = n^N\left(1 + N\frac{\tau^2}{T^2}\frac{Q}{12}\right),$$

where, when exchange coupling is neglected,

$$Q = 2N^{-2}\sum_{j\neq i} r_{ij}{}^{-6}.$$

The sums may be estimated by taking into account only the interaction between nearest neighbours. For cubic arrangements it is not very difficult to calculate the exact value. Van Vleck finds:

Simple cubic $\qquad Q_{sc} = 12 \times 1.40$,

Face centred cubic $\qquad Q_{fc} = 12 \times 1.20$,

Body centred cubic $\qquad Q_{bc} = \frac{256}{27} \times 1.53$.

For the internal energy we find

$$E = -Nk\frac{\tau^2}{T}\frac{2Q}{12},$$

and for the specific heat

$$C_m = Nk\frac{\tau^2}{T^2}\frac{2Q}{12}.$$

This is then the exact expression for the specific heat, the existence of which was explained in 5.4.

Van Vleck has also calculated the terms in the specific heat which are proportional to $(\tau/T)^3$ and $(\tau/T)^4$. We will not quote the results.

5.5². Influences of Stark splittings on magnetic specific heat.

The situation becomes much more complicated when Stark splittings are present. This will at once become clear when we consider the simple picture described in 5.4. For the moment of the ion itself will depend on temperature and so will the

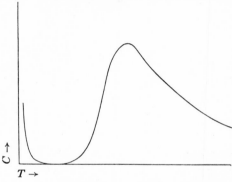

Fig. 9. Specific heat for a very dilute salt.

susceptibility of the surrounding medium. Only when $k\tau$ is very small compared to the Stark splittings so that all ions are in the lowest state before magnetic splitting becomes important, the situation will again be rather simple. Such a situation may occur in magnetically very dilute salts. The total specific heat will be represented by a curve of the type shown in fig. 9. The Stark specific heat will have decreased to zero before the magnetic specific heat becomes of any importance. This magnetic specific heat will then depend exclusively on the properties of the lowest Stark level (which, because of the existence of an odd number of spins will of course be degenerate). Further it can easily be shown that at temperatures where the $1/T^2$ law holds the specific heat is simply the sum of the Stark heat and the magnetic specific heat calculated for ions without Stark splittings.

In general, however, the situation will be quite different. Van Vleck has succeeded in calculating the first approximation of the magnetic specific heat, allowing rigorously for the existence of Stark levels. The expression for the magnetic energy will then depend in a complicated way on the temperature. The energy is not even always a monotonous function of temperature; at some temperatures the magnetic interaction may thus lead to a decrease of the total specific heat. The general feature of the specific heat curve, however, will be that the magnetic specific heat will start to increase rapidly before the Stark specific heat has become

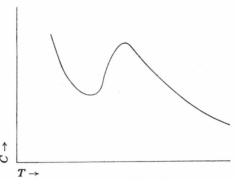

Fig. 10. Specific heat for a moderately dilute salt.

zero; this is shown in fig. 10. A behaviour of this type has really been found for the alums of iron and chromium.

Some of the results obtained by Van Vleck and his collaborators Hebb and Purcell are quoted in the next chapter.

5.6. The influence of magnetic interaction on the susceptibility.

The calculation of the magnetic moment leads to the following results. To a first approximation the influence of the interaction can be described by the Lorentz field. This result has been proved by Van Vleck in a very general way and it holds also in case of saturation and when Stark splittings are taken into account; of course when exchange interaction is not negligible an "exchange field" must be added to the purely magnetic Lorentz field.

But it is also found—in agreement with the results derived from Onsager's model—that in the next approximation the Lorentz field does no longer give correct results.

Van Vleck finds, neglecting exchange and Stark splittings, that in the Lorentz expression

$$\chi = \chi_0 \left[1 + \left(\frac{4\pi}{3} - \alpha \right) \chi_0 + \left(\frac{4\pi}{3} - \alpha \right)^2 \chi_0^2 + \dots \right],$$

the term $(4\pi/3 - \alpha)^2 \chi_0^2$ has to be replaced by

$$\left(\frac{4\pi}{3} - \alpha \right)^2 \chi_0^2 - \delta T^{-2},$$

where

$$\delta = \left[1 + \frac{3}{8J(J+1)} \right] Q \times \frac{\tau^2}{9}.$$

Remembering that $\chi_0 = \tau/3T$, we see that the expression

$$2 \times \left(\frac{4\pi}{3} \right)^2 \chi_0^2$$

occurring in Onsager's theory is now replaced by

$$\left[1 + \frac{3}{8J(J+1)} \right] Q \chi_0^2.$$

The difference is partly a quantum mechanical correction, vanishing at large J and partly due to the somewhat drastic simplification of the geometric arrangement of the ions, introduced by Onsager. The numerical difference, however, may be quite large: for a face-centred lattice $Q = 14 \cdot 4$, whereas $2(4\pi/3)^2 = 33$. Of course one may now try to correct Onsager's complete expression in such a way, that the term with χ_0^2 comes out correctly; this problem has been considered by Van Vleck. However, it is rather probable that such a formula will not give rigorous results.

We will not dwell here upon the question of the applicability of Onsager's formula to the case when Stark splittings occur, but confine ourselves to the rather conservative statement that the quantity $2 \times (4\pi/3)^2 \chi_0^2$ will certainly give the order of magnitude of the terms by which the Lorentz formula may be wrong. For several applications this is already a valuable statement.

5.6[1]. The problem of ferromagnetism.

From a theoretical point of view perhaps the most interesting question is, whether magnetic interaction leads to ferromagnetism. We shall see in the next chapter that from an experimental point of view there is as yet no conclusive evidence that in crystals showing "ferromagnetism" of the type described by Kürti and Simon exchange coupling is absent, although these crystals—mostly alums of ions of the iron group—are very dilute, which will tend to reduce exchange forces to zero. The anomalies found by Becquerel [3] and others for more concentrated salts are almost certainly connected with exchange forces.

The theory of magnetic interaction has not yet been sufficiently developed to give an answer to this question. The Lorentz formula leads to ferromagnetism. Indeed, if

$$H_i = H_0 + \frac{4\pi}{3} J - \alpha J,$$

and

$$J = \frac{a}{T} H_i,$$

so that

$$J = \frac{a H_0}{T - \left(\frac{4\pi}{3} - \alpha\right) a},$$

we see that the formula breaks down at the temperature

$$T = \left(\frac{4\pi}{3} - \alpha\right) a.$$

From there on one has to take into account saturation, and the equations

$$H_i = H_0 + \left(\frac{4\pi}{3} - \alpha\right) J$$

and

$$J = f(H_i/T)$$

can be solved by a graphical method analogous to that used in the Weiss theory. This type of ferromagnetism has been discussed in some detail by Debye. A remarkable point is, that the Curie temperature depends on the shape of the body and that for a sphere no ferromagnetism should occur. However, it is scarcely to be expected that this primitive theory will be in agreement with reality. In the first place we know that the Lorentz formula is not exact. Further we know that there exists a specific heat due to magnetic interaction, and this specific heat does *not* depend on the shape of the body. According to the results of Kürti and Simon just above the Curie point there is an enormous rise of the specific heat. This would rather suggest that the Curie point does not depend on the shape.

Onsager's complete formula on the other hand does not predict any magnetic anomalies.

Further it is evident that the determination of a number of coefficients in a series of powers of $1/T$ will never enable us to decide whether ferromagnetism will really occur. One can only say that if it occurs it will occur at a temperature where these asymptotic series cease to converge, that is at a temperature of the order τ. This is certainly in agreement with experimental results.

It is well known that in the case of ferromagnetism Heisenberg's original theory, which consists essentially in the determination of two coefficients in a series of powers of $1/T$, does *not* prove the existence of ferromagnetism at low temperatures, but fortunately in this case another approximation is possible: the Slater-Bloch theory which holds near $T = 0$. In the case of magnetic interaction one has not yet succeeded in finding such a way of approach.

In the theory of the equation of state of gases we meet with an analogous difficulty if we try to derive the existence of condensation. Only quite recently progress has been made. Still van der Waals was able to arrive at an equation which happened to account quite reasonably for the experimental facts, although the derivation could not at all be justified for very dense gases. Now a similar stroke of good luck might occur again. However, there is reason to suspect that neither the Lorentz formula nor the Onsager formula will serve the purpose.

We feel confident, however, that some day a mathematical

theory will be developed which will make it possible to give a rigorous answer to these questions.

5.7. Calculation in high fields.

We shall finally mention that Van Vleck (79) has calculated the thermodynamic functions for the case of *one* spin, taking into account only the first approximation of magnetic interaction, but allowing rigorously for saturation effects. These results will be quoted in the next chapter.

Chapter VI

SOME EXPERIMENTAL RESULTS

6.1. Introduction.

In this chapter we shall describe some of the results obtained with various substances and thus show in which way the theoretical considerations explained in preceding chapters may be used to discuss experimental results. However, our knowledge is still rather scanty. A further difficulty is, that some of the material has only been published in a preliminary form.

6.2. Substances where Stark splitting has no influence.

If we want to study the influence of magnetic interaction, it will be very advantageous to use a substance where the additional complication of the Stark effect does not arise. The ideal magnetic ion or atom would be an ion or atom with one s-electron outside a closed shell but unfortunately such a thing does not occur in solids. Almost as good, however, is the case of an ion with one non s-electron outside a closed shell, for here one may hope that the orbital moment will be quenched by the crystalline field. But here also there are not many possibilities. Three-valued cerium and three-valued titanium seem to be the only reasonable instances. De Haas and Wiersma have done a number of experiments with cerium salts and it is quite possible that ultimately cerium salts will again become important in demagnetization work. However, the situation is certainly *not* ideally simple; no complete quenching of orbits occurs in the liquid helium region. Three-valued titanium is usually not very stable, but fortunately the double sulphate with caesium (CsTi alum, $CsTi(SO_4)_2 . 12H_2O$) exists, and this substance was used by de Haas and Wiersma [44, 45]. With certain precautions it can be obtained in good crystals. It should be kept in a nitrogen or noble gas atmosphere, otherwise the titanium is oxidized. The equilibrium pressure of the water vapour is of the same order as for the other alums and care should be taken to avoid dehydration. For the crystal structure of the alums cf. (71).

The possibilities of finding a substance where Stark splitting has no influence are, however, not exhausted. Thus according to Kramers' theorem there will exist in all ions with an odd number of electrons a doubly degenerate lowest Stark level; one has only to look for substances where the distance to the next higher level is large compared with $1°$ K., whereas the magnetic interaction is small. Some of the complex ions might be useful. It is also not quite unthinkable that there exists a chromium compound where the Stark splitting is so large as to fulfil the requirements formulated above.

Also copper salts, for instance $CuSO_4 . 5H_2O$, might give interesting results. Here one electron is missing from a complete d-shell, there is a positive hole in a d-state. However, measurements on the anisotropy by Krishnan (52) and co-workers indicate that the magnetism cannot completely be described as spin-only magnetism.

6.2¹. Properties of CsTi alum.

For the time being CsTi alum seems to be the only substance which may be expected to have one-spin-only magnetism. It is then somewhat disconcerting to find, that next to nothing is known concerning the magnetic susceptibility of this substance. From de Haas and Wiersma's demagnetization experiments we may infer that Curie's law is followed in the liquid helium region; this is also shown by experiments of de Haas and du Pré and the susceptibility is also of the expected order of magnitude. But the distance to the next Stark level is not even approximately known and—even more important—we do not know whether the moment corresponds really to one Bohr magneton. Direct measurements are highly desirable and it will be seen that the theoretical discussion of the experimental results of adiabatic demagnetization experiments is rendered unnecessarily uncertain by our lack of experimental knowledge.

In the following we will provisionally assume that the magnetic moment is one Bohr magneton.

The molecular weight is 589·2 and for the susceptibility per gram it follows

$$\chi_{\text{gr.}} = \frac{4s(s+1)}{3T} \times \frac{3 \cdot 7237}{5892} = \frac{1}{T} \times 6 \cdot 320 \times 10^{-4},$$

and, assuming a density 2,

$$\chi = \frac{1}{T} \times 1 \cdot 264 \times 10^{-3}.$$

Writing

$$\chi = \frac{\tau}{3T},$$

we find

$$\tau = 0 \cdot 0038.$$

Since τ is very small the second order correction to the susceptibility will become important only at very low temperatures. Since the magnetic ions form a face-centred cubic lattice we have (compare 5.6)

$$\delta = \left(1 + \frac{3}{6}\right) \frac{14 \cdot 4}{9} \times (0 \cdot 0038)^2,$$

when, for a sphere,

$$\frac{M}{H_0} = \frac{\tau}{3T} \left(1 - \frac{\delta}{T^2}\right).$$

At 0·04° K. this correction amounts to only 2·4 %.

The specific heat is given theoretically by

$$\frac{C_m}{R} = 2 \cdot 40 \left(\frac{\tau}{T}\right)^2 - 4 \cdot 35 \left(\frac{\tau}{T}\right)^3 - 13 \cdot 5 \left(\frac{\tau}{T}\right)^4 + \dots.$$

Hebb and Purcell found satisfactory agreement with unpublished data of Kürti and Simon, using only the first term of the expansion.

It seems to the author that very accurate results might be obtained by demagnetization experiments starting from low fields; the case seems very suitable for applying the formulae derived in 5.4[1].

De Haas and Wiersma have determined the magnetic moment in a number of final fields; the initial field was of the order of

24,000 G. and the initial temperature $1 \cdot 17^\circ$ K. Their results are shown in fig. 11. The theoretical values obtained by Van Vleck [79] are shown also in this diagram. The solid curves were calculated using the formula

$$\frac{M}{M_0} = \frac{H}{\sqrt{B+H^2}} \Big/ \frac{H_0}{\sqrt{B+H_0^2}},$$

with $B = 0 \cdot 774 \times 10^4$. For initial fields of 7000 G. and lower this gives sufficient agreement with the more accurate calculations of Van Vleck.

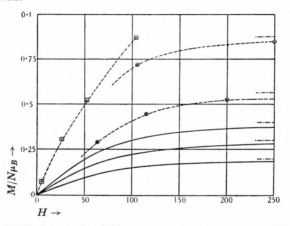

Fig. 11. M, H-diagram for CsTi alum. ⊡ measured; ⊙ calculated (Van Vleck); solid curve, elementary theory; $- \cdot - \cdot -$ value in initial field

It will be seen that there is no agreement between theory and experiment, and also that it is very difficult to draw a reasonable curve through the points of de Haas and Wiersma, if we assume that the initial moment is really given by the value shown in the figure, which was calculated from the saturation curve for one Bohr magneton. So we believe that either the experiments contain some error or that the magnetic moment is considerably smaller than a Bohr magneton. Under these circumstances it is hardly justified to apply the relation $H/H_0 = T/T_0$, although it will certainly give the right order of magnitude of T. According to Van Vleck it should be wrong by 11 %.

We sum up the situation:

(a) It is extremely probable that caesium-titanium alum is a. very ideal paramagnetic substance, and that the temperatures derived by extrapolating Curie's law are accurate to within 1 % down to a few hundredths of a degree.

(b) It is necessary thoroughly to investigate the susceptibility between 1 and 300° K.

(c) It is desirable to carry out demagnetization experiments starting at low fields in order to check the theory and especially in order to decide whether there is any exchange coupling. If agreement with theory is obtained, then the magnetic temperature scale would become entirely trustworthy.

(d) It is desirable to repeat the measurement of de Haas and Wiersma and to use slightly higher final fields. If it is found that M can be represented by a formula of the form

$$M = M_0 - \frac{f(H_0, T_0)}{H^2},$$

then the application of the relation $T/T_0 = H/H_0$ becomes reliable and corrections can be estimated theoretically. This would also be very important for the determination of the thermodynamic temperature scale.

6.3. Potassium-chromium alum.

Perhaps the most useful substance for studying the influence of Stark splittings would be $KCr(SO_4)_2 . 12H_2O$. The molecular weight is 499·4, the density 1·83. Further

$$\chi_{gr.} = \frac{1}{T} \times 3\cdot73 \times 10^{-3},$$

$$\chi = \frac{1}{T} \times 6\cdot81 \times 10^{-3},$$

$$\tau = 0\cdot0204° \text{ K}.$$

The susceptibility has been measured rather accurately by de Haas, Gorter and van den Handel [23, 34] and is in good agreement with the theoretical values.

Now if the constant A in the equation

$$C/R = A/T^2 + BT^3$$

were accurately known, it would be possible at once to derive the distance between the two Stark levels. Unfortunately no

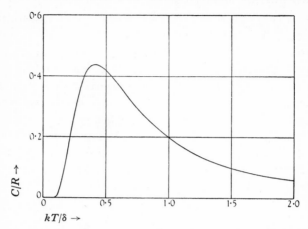

Fig. 12. Specific heat of KCr alum (in units R) as a function of kT/δ.

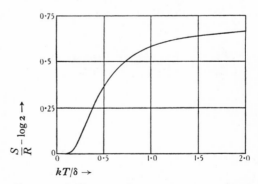

Fig. 13. Entropy of KCr alum (in units R) as a function of kT/δ.

measurements of this type exist. Hebb and Purcell[48] have assumed a splitting of 0·20° K. to account for unpublished work of Kürti and Simon on the specific heat, but from a result of de Haas and Wiersma, who state that an initial field of 4100 G. and a temperature of $1 \cdot 21°$ K. lead to a final temperature of $0 \cdot 270°$ K., we find a much larger splitting ($\delta/k = 0 \cdot 27°$ K.). So the situation is rather uncertain. Once the splitting is known the Stark specific heat and entropy can easily be calculated. They are shown in figs. 12 and 13. Further, if it is assumed that the lowest level is the level with angular momentum $3/2$ and $-3/2$ in the direction of the trigonal axis, the correction to the susceptibility can be calculated (fig. 14).

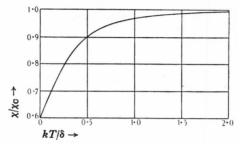

Fig. 14. Correction factor, χ/χ_{Curie}, as a function of kT/δ.

To the entropy must be added the contribution due to magnetic interaction which according to Hebb and Purcell is given by

$$S_{\text{magn.}} = R\tau^2 \frac{d}{dT}\left(\frac{\Omega}{T}\right)$$

with

$$\Omega = \frac{1 \cdot 20}{Z^2/4}\left\{\left(\frac{3}{50}+\frac{223}{150}\frac{kT}{\delta}\right)\right.$$
$$\left.+\left(\frac{88}{75}+\frac{8}{15}\frac{kT}{\delta}\right)e^{-\delta/kT}+\left(\frac{49}{150}-\frac{143}{150}\frac{kT}{\delta}\right)e^{-2\delta/kT}\right\}.$$

A corresponding correction must be added to the specific heat. Down to $0 \cdot 1°$ K. this correction is relatively small. At still lower temperatures, however, the specific heat will again increase. Qualitatively this is in agreement with the results of Kürti and Simon.

Of course at these very low temperatures the Lorentz formula will no longer be reliable.

The main advantage of potassium-chromium alum as compared to other salts is on the one hand that the Stark pattern is extremely simple, on the other hand that τ is rather small compared with the Stark splitting, so that we are well below the maximum of Stark specific heat before the magnetic specific heat becomes important.

6.3¹. Diluted chromium salts.

By using still more diluted chromium salts it will be possible to obtain still lower values of τ and thus shift the magnetic hump in the specific heat to still lower temperatures. De Haas and Wiersma (43) have used a mixed crystal of aluminium and chromium alum containing 1 Cr with 14·4 Al. Now as long as the magnetization entropy remains below $R^e\log 2$ some of the ions will still remain in the upper Stark state and the temperature reached will not be lower than for an undiluted alum. Perhaps it will even be higher, for the fact that the symmetry of the crystal is slightly spoilt may lead to a higher Stark splitting. In a lecture given at Leiden, Simon has indeed reported to have found such an increase of the Stark separation. But as soon as the entropy of magnetization exceeds $R^e\log 2$ we shall obtain much lower temperatures in the case of the diluted salt. Indeed, de Haas and Wiersma found that for a field of 12,000 G. at 1·20° K. there is no big difference between diluted and undiluted alum, but a field of 24,000 G. leads in the case of the diluted substance to an extremely low temperature: $T^* = 0\cdot0043$.

6.4. Iron-ammonium alum.

This substance, the first data on which were published by Simon, has been very frequently used, and Kürti and Simon have published observations on the specific heat, the ferromagnetism and the thermodynamic scale. From a theoretical point of view the situation is slightly more complicated than in the case of potassium-chromium alum. Hebb and Purcell, assuming a doubly degenerate lowest Stark level and a fourfold degenerate upper one, found a splitting of 0·225° K. Since $\tau = 0\cdot0472$ the two humps are here much closer together. We refer to the original publications for a closer discussion of the properties of this substance.

6.5. Gadolinium sulphate.

Gadolinium sulphate $Gd_2(SO_4)_3 \cdot 7H_2O$ was the first substance for which a saturation curve was obtained. The measurements are often referred to as the "classical investigations of Woltjer and Kamerlingh Onnes[83]"; from the point of view of modern experimental technique, however, they are not completely satisfactory. As far as the measurements go there is agreement with the theoretical formula.

The density at $15°$ C. is $3 \cdot 013$ and the molecular weight $373 \cdot 5$.

Specific heat measurements have been carried out by various authors. In the table we give the specific heat measured by Clark and Keesom[8] (or rather the values of C/R for one gram ion) together with the values calculated from the formula

$$C/R = A/T^2 + BT^3,$$

with

$$A = 0 \cdot 282$$

and

$$B = 14 \cdot 6 \times 10^{-5}.$$

T	$(C/R)_{\text{exp.}}$	$(C/R)_{\text{calc.}}$
20	$1 \cdot 133$	$1 \cdot 169$
15	$0 \cdot 533$	$0 \cdot 494$
10	$0 \cdot 151$	$0 \cdot 149$
8	$0 \cdot 078$	$0 \cdot 079$
6	$0 \cdot 041$	$0 \cdot 039$
5	$0 \cdot 031$	$0 \cdot 030$
4·5	$0 \cdot 028$	$0 \cdot 028$
4	$0 \cdot 027$	$0 \cdot 027$
3·5	$0 \cdot 029$	$0 \cdot 030$
3	$0 \cdot 035$	$0 \cdot 035$
2·5	$0 \cdot 050$	$0 \cdot 047$
2	$0 \cdot 071^5$	$0 \cdot 071^5$
1·5	$0 \cdot 125$	$0 \cdot 126$
1	$0 \cdot 222$	$0 \cdot 286$

The value of B corresponds to a lattice specific heat of $98T^3$ erg/c.c. which is very reasonable. From the value of A we can now deduce a value for the overall Stark splitting. We have, assuming a cubic field,

$$A = \frac{33}{256}\left(\frac{\delta}{k}\right)^2 + 2 \cdot 4\tau^2,$$

and since $\tau = 0 \cdot 189$, it follows $\delta/k = 1 \cdot 25°$ K.

On the other hand, Giauque and MacDougall have determined a number of points in the entropy diagram and Hebb and Purcell found that these points can be reasonably explained by assuming $\delta/k = 1\cdot4°$ K. We believe that the value $1\cdot25$ is more reliable.

6.5^1. Diluted gadolinium salts.

Giauque and collaborators have also investigated two more diluted gadolinium salts, viz. $Gd(C_6H_4NO_2SO_3).7H_2O$ and $Gd(PMo_{12}O_{40}).30H_2O$.

It should be pointed out that there is one great advantage in diluting by making complicated compounds; the distribution of Gd ions will be uniform. On the other hand there is no reason at all, that the Stark splittings should be identical in all compounds. Hebb and Purcell have shown that the entropy diagram of $Gd(C_6H_4NO_2SO_3).7H_2O$ can be explained by assuming $\delta/k = 1\cdot4°$ K and neglecting magnetic interaction ($\tau \sim 0\cdot05$). We do not think that there is any reason why δ/k should also be $1\cdot4$ for gadolinium sulphate although it is satisfactory that the order of magnitude is correct.

In the case of gadolinium phosphomolybdate, however, a different parameter is found. In the liquid helium region the specific heat (determined partly by demagnetization experiments and partly by heating with an induction heater) can again be represented by a formula

$$C/R = A/T^2 + BT^3,$$

with $$A = 0\cdot118$$
and $$B = 3\cdot42 \times 10^{-3},$$

as will be seen from our table:

T	$(C/R)_{exp.}$	$(C/R)_{calc.}$	T	$(C/R)_{exp.}$	$(C/R)_{calc.}$
3·81	0·198	0·197	1·34	0·0725	0·074
3·72	0·175	0·185	1·34	0·0745	0·074
2·98	0·105	0·104	1·266	0·080	0·080^5
2·40	0·067	0·068	1·260	0·081	0·081
2·11	0·062	0·059	1·257	0·087	0·082
2·06	0·055	0·058	1·150	0·100	0·094
1·90	0·068	0·056	1·134	0·084	0·096^4

The magnetic interaction is entirely negligible and, again assuming cubic symmetry, it follows:

$$\frac{33}{256}\left(\frac{\delta}{k}\right)^2 = 0.118$$

or $\delta/k = 0.96°$ K. It would certainly be worth while to try whether the other results of Giauque and MacDougall on the entropy at lower temperatures and on adiabatic M, H-curves can be explained using this value of δ.

We are convinced, however, that the fact that further dilution has in this case caused a lower value of δ is somewhat accidental and that there is no reason to suppose that at still further dilution still lower values of δ will be obtained.

6.6. Summary.

In the preceding section we have discussed a few experiments and it will be seen that the situation is far from satisfactory. For none of the substances have we arrived at a complete description, not even in the region of temperatures where the higher approximations of the magnetic interaction are not yet important, so that there are no serious theoretical difficulties. From a theoretical point of view the influence of this magnetic interaction, especially the occurrence of "ferromagnetism" is perhaps the most interesting topic, but unless we want to restrict the investigation of this phenomenon entirely to CsTi alum—which has experimental disadvantages—a thorough knowledge of the Stark pattern will be necessary. We believe that in this connection more attention should be given to KCr alum, since in the case of iron a trigonal field may perhaps lead to complications.

From a theoretical point of view Gd has the disadvantage, that the number of indetermined constants which enter the theory as soon as other than cubic fields are admitted, is large. From an experimental point of view Gd has the disadvantage that it is very expensive; and one cannot easily obtain very low temperatures. However, in view of the very careful and extensive measurements of Giauque and MacDougall, it would certainly be worth while to develop the theory somewhat further than has been done until now.

Chapter VII

RELAXATION PHENOMENA

7.1. Introduction.

Until now we have always tacitly assumed that the para-magnetic salt is in a state of equilibrium. If A.C. measurements are carried out this is no longer evident and even ballistic measurements might be influenced by time effects. To discuss the different possibilities we will treat the paramagnetic salt as consisting of two coupled systems: on the one hand there is the system of magnetic ions, with its Stark splittings and magnetic interactions ("spin-system"), on the other hand the system of lattice vibrations. Now it may be that there is no thermal equilibrium within the spin-system and there may be equilibrium between the spins but no equilibrium between the spins and the lattice. Finally also the lattice itself might be in a state of non-equilibrium.

7.2. Discussion assuming spin-equilibrium (6, 32, 55).

We will first assume that the system of magnetic ions is in thermal equilibrium within itself, so that we can define a spin-temperature T_s which may be different, however, from the lattice temperature T_l. Such an assumption will be reasonable when the time necessary for establishing the equilibrium in the spin-system is short compared with the time necessary for establishing the equilibrium between spin and lattice, and when the external parameters do not appreciably change during the time necessary for establishing spin-equilibrium. Under these assumptions it is easy to write down the equations which will describe the relaxation phenomena. Indeed, the heat supplied to the spin-system in a time dt will be proportional to the temperature difference $T_l - T_s$, at least when this temperature difference is small,

$$dQ = \kappa(T_l - T_s)\,dt.$$

The quantity κ may still depend on temperature and on the magnetic field. Writing U_s for the interior energy of the spin-system, we have

$$\kappa(T_l - T_s)\, dt = dU_s - H\, dM;$$

further

$$M = f(H, T),$$

and, by 2.11,

$$U_s(H, T) = U_s(0, T) + \int_0^H \left(T\frac{\partial M}{\partial T} + H\frac{\partial M}{\partial H} \right) dH.$$

These equations contain in principle a complete theory of the relaxation phenomena as long as the assumptions formulated above are valid.

7.2[1]. Lattice at constant temperature.

We will first assume, that the lattice is kept at constant temperature; this will be the case when the crystals are immersed in liquid helium and the crystals are sufficiently small.

Let us suppose that the substance is placed in a constant magnetic field H_0 on which is superimposed an alternating field in the same direction

$$H = H_0 + h = H_0 + h_0 e^{i\omega t}:$$

we will assume that h is small and neglect higher powers; further we put

$$M = M(H_0, T_l) + m = M_0 + m_0 e^{i\omega t},$$

and

$$T_s - T_l = \vartheta = \vartheta_0 e^{i\omega t}.$$

Substituting in the equations of the preceding section

$$-\kappa\vartheta\, dt = dU_s - H\, dM,$$

$$-\kappa\vartheta\, dt = \left(\frac{\partial U_s}{\partial H} - H\frac{\partial M}{\partial H} \right) dh + \left(\frac{\partial U_s}{\partial T} - H\frac{\partial M}{\partial T} \right) d\vartheta,$$

and hence

$$\vartheta = \frac{\dfrac{\partial U_s}{\partial H} - H\dfrac{\partial M}{\partial H}}{-\dfrac{\kappa}{i\omega} - \left(\dfrac{\partial U_s}{\partial T} - H\dfrac{\partial M}{\partial T} \right)}\, h = \frac{T\dfrac{\partial M}{\partial T}}{C_H} \cdot \frac{1}{-\dfrac{\rho}{i\omega} - 1}\, h,$$

where we have put

$$C_H = \frac{\partial U_s}{\partial T} - H\frac{\partial M}{\partial T}$$

and

$$\rho = \kappa/C_H;$$

C_H is the specific heat at constant exterior field. We can use the expression for ϑ to calculate m:

$$m = \left[\left(\frac{\partial M}{\partial H} \right)_T + \left(\frac{\partial M}{\partial T} \right)_H \frac{T \left(\frac{\partial M}{\partial T} \right)_H}{C_H} \cdot \frac{1}{-\dfrac{\rho}{i\omega} - 1} \right] h.$$

Now let us write $(\partial M/\partial H)_u$ for the ratio m/h when $\rho = 0$, that is, when there is no coupling between spin and lattice; when the lattice specific heat can be neglected this is also the value which will be obtained when static adiabatic measurements are carried out. Then we can write

$$m = \left[\left(\frac{\partial M}{\partial H} \right)_u + \left\{ \left(\frac{\partial M}{\partial H} \right)_T - \left(\frac{\partial M}{\partial H} \right)_u \right\} \frac{1}{1 + i\omega/\rho} \right] h. \quad (1)$$

We find that the magnetization in an alternating field can be described by a simple dispersion formula. For low measuring frequencies $(\omega \ll \rho)$ we find for the susceptibility the isothermal value $(\partial M/\partial H)_T$, for high frequencies on the other hand we find a value as if there were no coupling. For intermediate values we find a complex susceptibility: there is a phase lag between the moment and the field. A very elegant form of equation (1) has been derived by Debye [12].

The meaning of ρ will become clearer if we consider the following problem. Suppose, that at the time $t = 0$ the magnetic field is suddenly changed, but then left constant. The spin-temperature will also suffer a sudden change and then gradually get back to T_l. We have

$$-\kappa\vartheta = C_H \frac{d\vartheta}{dt},$$

and hence $\qquad\qquad \vartheta = \vartheta_{t=0} e^{-t\rho}.$

We see that $1/\rho$ is the time constant describing the restoring of the equilibrium.

A very simple equation is obtained when we assume that Curie's law holds,

$$M = aH/T,$$

and that the specific heat is given by $C = A/T^2$, for then (5.4^1)

$$\left(\frac{\partial M}{\partial H}\right)_u = \left(\frac{\partial M}{\partial H}\right)_T \frac{A}{A + aH^2}. \qquad (2)$$

It is interesting to notice, that in very low fields no relaxation occurs even when ρ is finite. This is connected with the circumstance discussed in 3.4 that in very low fields the magnetization is possible without a change of the distribution of the magnetic ions.

7.2². Experimental results.

De Haas and du Pré [47] have measured the value of the real part of m/h for iron-ammonium alum in the liquid helium region, using frequencies between 20 and 60 cycles; du Pré and the author have shown that the results are in satisfactory agreement with the equations (1) and (2) of the preceding section. The relaxation time $1/\rho$ is of the order 10^{-2} sec. and ρ increases roughly with the square of the temperature. Since measurements of this type can be performed with a considerable degree of accuracy it is to be expected that ultimately they will not only lead to an accurate determination of ρ as a function of H and T but also to a reliable determination of the constant A.

For CsTi alum no relaxation phenomena were found at 60 cycles; de Haas and du Pré [47a] infer that for this substance $(1/\rho) < 10^{-3}$ sec.

The first relaxation measurements of the type described here, were carried out by Gorter and Brons [26-31] at nitrogen temperatures. They used the heterodyne beat method and worked at frequencies of the order of 10^6. Although the curves obtained are roughly speaking of the same type as those of de Haas and du Pré the situation is probably less simple, except perhaps at the lowest nitrogen temperature. It seems that the assumption of spin-equilibrium is at these high frequencies not completely justified. Also Gorter and Brons were unable to find any relaxation effect for CsTi alum.

7.3. Variable lattice temperature.

Let us now suppose, that the lattice is not kept at constant temperature; let C_L be the specific heat of the lattice (or of the lattice together with a heat container connected to the lattice) and let T_0 be the average temperature in the case of an alternating exterior field. We put $T_s - T_l = \vartheta$ and $T_l - T_0 = \vartheta_l$. To the equations of 7.2[1] we must now add the equation

$$C_L \frac{d\vartheta_l}{dt} = \kappa\vartheta.$$

We shall first investigate the way in which equilibrium is restored in a constant magnetic field. We have

$$-\kappa\vartheta = C_H\left(\frac{d\vartheta}{dt} + \frac{d\vartheta_l}{dt}\right),$$

and hence

$$\frac{d\vartheta}{dt} = -\kappa\left(\frac{\mathrm{I}}{C_H} + \frac{\mathrm{I}}{C_L}\right)\vartheta,$$

and

$$\vartheta = \vartheta_{t=0}\,e^{-\rho_1 t}$$

with

$$\rho_1 = \kappa\left(\frac{\mathrm{I}}{C_H} + \frac{\mathrm{I}}{C_L}\right).$$

Equilibrium is restored in a shorter time than in the case when the lattice is kept at constant temperature, and the lower the lattice specific heat the shorter the time. We will in a later section discuss the order of magnitude which may be expected.

We shall further discuss the case of a periodic field. Again there will be two extreme cases: when ω is large we obtain the value for "uncoupled" spin and lattice,

$$\left(\frac{\partial M}{\partial H}\right)_u = \left(\frac{\partial M}{\partial H}\right)_T - \frac{T\left(\frac{\partial M}{\partial T}\right)_H^2}{C_H};$$

and for small ω we obtain the adiabatic value

$$\left(\frac{\partial M}{\partial H}\right)_{ad} = \left(\frac{\partial M}{\partial H}\right)_T - \frac{T\left(\frac{\partial M}{\partial T}\right)_H^2}{C_L + C_H}.$$

A simple calculation shows that for an exterior field of the form

$$H = H_0 + h_0 e^{i\omega t},$$

we have $$M = M_0 + m$$

with $$m = \left[\left(\frac{\partial M}{\partial H} \right)_u + \left\{ \left(\frac{\partial M}{\partial H} \right)_{ud} - \left(\frac{\partial M}{\partial H} \right)_u \right\} \frac{1}{1 + i\omega/\rho_1} \right] h.$$

This formula is of exactly the same form as that derived in 7.2[1], only the constant ρ_1 is larger by a factor $(C_L + C_H)/C_L$ and that part of the magnetization that shows relaxation is smaller by a factor $C_L/(C_L + C_H)$.

7.3[1]. Spin-lattice equilibrium.

Very soon after the first successful experiments on the production of very low temperatures by the magnetic method had been carried out, the question arose, whether the lattice temperature will follow the spin temperature or not. The question is all important if one wants to apply the demagnetization method to the investigation of the properties of other substances at very low temperatures. The time lag in the lattice temperature will be of the order $1/\rho_1 = C_L/(C_L + C_H)\rho$. Now the factor $C_L/(C_L + C_H)$ will always be very small and decrease rapidly, when the temperature is lowered. Indeed, we shall have $C_L = BT^3$ and B will nearly always be smaller than 100 erg/gram. On the other hand C_H will be given by

$$C_H = \frac{A + aH^2}{T^2}.$$

For one gram of iron-ammonium alum at $1°$ K. the second term is roughly 10^4 in a field of 1000 G.; the first term is of the order 2×10^3. According to the results of de Haas and du Pré $1/\rho$ is of the order 10^{-2} sec. at $1°$ K. and hence $1/\rho_1$ is of the order 10^{-4}. Unless ρ decreases more rapidly than $C_L/(C_L + C_H)$ which is extremely improbable since in the helium region $\rho \sim T^2$, the time $1/\rho_1$ will become shorter and not longer at lower temperatures. So we can safely predict that the temperature of the lattice will always immediately follow the temperature of the spin-system. It is interesting to note that Heitler and Teller [49] in a paper on this subject arrived at an opposite conclusion because they failed to distinguish between the constants ρ and ρ_1 and therefore neglected the factor $C_L/(C_L + C_H)$.

The only direct investigation on this question was carried out by Allen and Shire [1,2]. They determined the lattice temperature by measuring the resistance of a phosphor-bronze wire fixed to the salt with shellac. They found that the lattice temperature follows the spin-temperature in a time which was certainly much smaller than one second, but a time lag of the order of a second was found when the salt was placed in a capsule containing liquid helium. Perhaps—as was suggested by H. London during a discussion at the Cambridge meeting of the British Association—this was due to the increase in C_L caused by the presence of the liquid helium.

7.3². Heating effects.

The existence of a "complex" susceptibility will cause an irreversible heating effect. Indeed, if the magnetic field is given by

$$H = H_0 + Re(h_0 e^{i\omega t}),$$

and the moment by

$$M_0 + Re(m) \quad \text{with} \quad m = (\chi' + i\chi'')h,$$

an energy $-\frac{1}{2}\omega\chi''h_0^2$ will be dissipated per second and this will have exactly the same influence as when an amount of heat

$$\Delta Q = -\frac{1}{2}\omega\chi''h_0^2$$

is supplied per second. Using the formulae of the preceding section we find

$$\Delta Q = \frac{1}{2}h_0^2 \frac{\omega^2/\rho_1}{1 + \omega^2/\rho_1^2} \frac{C_L}{C_L + C_H} \left[\left(\frac{\partial M}{\partial H}\right)_T - \left(\frac{\partial M}{\partial H}\right)_u \right].$$

This shows that at a temperature of $1°$ K., and *a fortiori* at lower temperatures, the heating effects are comparatively small. It is especially interesting to notice, that for iron-ammonium alum in a field of 1000 G. and at $1°$ K. with 50 cycles, only a small heating effect would be obtained, and that this heating effect would be increased by bringing the salt into contact with some non-magnetic substance, so that C_L is increased.

7.4. Theory of spin-lattice equilibrium.

The theoretical discussion of spin-lattice equilibrium becomes comparatively simple when the exterior field is so large that there is a complete "Paschen-Back" effect, so that we can regard the different spins as independent systems. In that case

$$(\partial M/\partial H)_u = 0.$$

We have then to calculate the probability that one spin changes its direction, emitting or absorbing a quantum of the lattice vibrations. The constant ρ is proportional to the probability for such a process. We shall consider only the case of a spin $1/2$. Suppose that N_+ ions are directed parallel to the field and $N_- = N - N_+$ ions antiparallel to the field. We have

$$\frac{dN_+}{dt} = a_{+-} N_- - a_{-+} N_+,$$

$$\frac{dN_-}{dt} = a_{-+} N_+ - a_{+-} N_-.$$

Since in a state of equilibrium $N_+/N_- = e^{2H\mu/kT}$, the transition probabilities a_{+-} and a_{-+} have to fulfil the equation

$$a_{+-} = e^{2H\mu/kT} a_{-+},$$

whence $\quad \dfrac{dN_+}{dt} = -(a_{-+})[N_+ - e^{2H\mu/kT}(N - N_+)],$

or $\quad \dfrac{dN_+}{dt} = a_{-+}(1 + e^{2H\mu/kT})\left[N_+ - \dfrac{e^{2H\mu/kT}}{e^{2H\mu/kT} + 1} N\right].$

It follows, that

$$\rho = a_{-+}(1 + e^{2H\mu/kT}).$$

The probability a_{-+} was calculated by Waller, taking into account magnetic interaction between the spins. The coupling between spin and lattice is due to the fact that the magnetic interaction will change when the distances in the lattice change. Later also Heitler and Teller have considered this problem and they have tried also to take into account the electric interaction between the magnetic ion and the neighbouring ions.

The calculations lead to a relaxation time which is much larger than the time found experimentally. Further they do not at all explain the curious behaviour of CsTi alum. Recently considerable progress has been made by Kronig and by Van Vleck, but their papers have not yet been published. We will therefore omit a further discussion of the mechanism of the energy exchange. It is interesting to mention, that even if the estimate of Heitler and Teller were correct, the time $1/\rho_1$ would still be quite short. (Compare further, (80), (49), (14).)

7.5. Spin-spin equilibrium.

We must now say a few words concerning the question whether the spins themselves will always be in equilibrium. Gorter (24), in his well-known experiments, which were the starting point for this field of research, has shown that in the hydrogen region a heating effect occurs in an alternating field of 10^9 cycles, and this must certainly be due to relaxation in the spin-system, since lack of coupling with the lattice will in this case ($H_0 = 0$) have no influence. The relaxation time is of the order of magnitude predicted by theory (Waller (80)). The theory of these effects has been considered in more detail by Kronig and Gorter (33, 53).

At very low temperatures, however, this relaxation time seems to become much longer. Cooke and Hull (9) found for iron-ammonium alum below $1°$ K. a heating effect by an alternating field which was proportional to the square of the frequency, and hence must be ascribed to a relaxation time. This relaxation time shows a rapid increase when the temperature decreases toward the Curie point. A closer investigation of this effect might help to throw light on the nature of ferromagnetism.

The problem, whether in a constant exterior field the assumption of spin-equilibrium is justified, was considered by Kronig and Bouwkamp (54). However, we will not discuss this question further. It was the main purpose of this chapter to discuss the relaxation phenomena in connection with the technique of very low temperature research; for a general discussion of this subject we refer to the papers of Gorter, Kronig and their collaborators.

REFERENCES

(1) J. F. Allen and E. S. Shire. *Nature*, **139**, 878 (1937).
(2) J. F. Allen and E. S. Shire. *Proc. Camb. Phil. Soc.* **34**, 301 (1938).
(3) J. Becquerel and J. van den Handel. *Journ. d. Phys.* **10**, 1 (1939).
(4) G. Breit. *Proc. Roy. Ac. Amst.* **25**, 293 (1922); Leiden Comm. Suppl. 46.
(5) F. Brons. Dissertation, Groningen, 1938.
(6) H. B. G. Casimir and F. K. du Pré. *Physica*, **5**, 507 (1938); Comm. Suppl. 85*a*.
(7) C. W. Clark. Dissertation, Leiden, 1935.
(8) C. W. Clark and W. H. Keesom. *Physica*, **2**, 1075 (1935); Comm. 240*a*.
(9) A. H. Cooke and R. A. Hull. *Proc. Roy. Soc.* **162**, 404 (1937).
(10) P. Debye. *Ann. Phys.* **81**, 1154 (1926).
(11) P. Debye. *Phys. Z.* **35**, 923 (1934).
(12) P. Debye. *Phys. Z.* **39**, 616 (1938).
(13) P. Debye. *Ann. Phys.* **32**, 85 (1938).
(14) M. Fierz. *Physica*, **5**, 433 (1938).
(15) W. F. Giauque. *Journ. Am. Chem. Soc.* **49**, 1864, 1870 (1927).
(16) W. F. Giauque and D. P. MacDougall. *Phys. Rev.* **43**, 768 (1933).
(17) W. F. Giauque and D. P. MacDougall. *Phys. Rev.* **44**, 235 (1933).
(18) W. F. Giauque and D. P. MacDougall. *Journ. Am. Chem. Soc.* **57**, 1175 (1935).
(19) D. P. MacDougall and W. F. Giauque. *Journ. Am. Chem. Soc.* **58**, 1032 (1936).
(20) W. F. Giauque and D. P. MacDougall. *Journ. Am. Chem. Soc.* **60**, 376 (1936).
(21) W. F. Giauque, J. W. Stout and C. W. Clark. *Journ. Am. Chem. Soc.* **60**, 1053 (1938).
(22) C. J. Gorter. Dissertation, Leiden, 1932.
(23) C. J. Gorter, W. J. de Haas and J. van den Handel. *Proc. Kon. Ak. Amst.* **36**, 158 (1933); Comm. 222*d*.
(24) C. J. Gorter. *Physica*, **3**, 503 (1936).
(25) C. J. Gorter. *Physica*, **3**, 1006 (1936).
(26) C. J. Gorter and F. Brons. *Physica*, **4**, 579 (1937).
(27) C. J. Gorter and F. Brons. *Physica*, **4**, 667 (1937).
(28) F. Brons and C. J. Gorter. *Physica*, **5** (1938).
(29) F. Brons and C. J. Gorter. *Nature*, **141**, 369 (1938).
(30) P. Teunissen and C. J. Gorter. *Physica*, **5**, 486 (1938).
(31) C. J. Gorter, P. Teunissen and F. Brons. *Physica*, **5**, 657 (1938).
(32) C. J. Gorter. *Phys. Z.* **39**, 815 (1938).
(33) C. J. Gorter and R. de L. Kronig. *Physica*, **3**, 1009 (1936).
(34) W. J. de Haas and C. J. Gorter. *Proc. Kon. Ak. Amst.* **33**, 676 (1930); Comm. 208*c*.

(35) W. J. de Haas, E. C. Wiersma and H. A. Kramers. *Physica*, **13**, 175 (1933).
(36) W. J. de Haas, E. C. Wiersma and H. A. Kramers. *Nature*, **131**, 719 (1933).
(37) W. J. de Haas, E. C. Wiersma and H. A. Kramers. *Naturw.* **21**, 732 (1933).
(38) W. J. de Haas. *Nature*, **132**, 372 (1933).
(39) W. J. de Haas. *Naturw.* **21**, 732 (1933).
(40) W. J. de Haas, E. C. Wiersma and H. A. Kramers. *Physica*, **1**, 1 (1933); Comm. 229*a*.
(41) W. J. de Haas and E. C. Wiersma. *Physica*, **1**, 779 (1933); Comm. 231*e*.
(42) W. J. de Haas and E. C. Wiersma. *Physica*, **2**, 81 (1935); Comm. 236*a*.
(43) W. J. de Haas and E. C. Wiersma. *Physica*, **2**, 235 (1935); Comm. 236*b*.
(44) W. J. de Haas and E. C. Wiersma. *Physica*, **2**, 438 (1935); Comm. 236*c*.
(45) W. J. de Haas and E. C. Wiersma. *Physica*, **3**, 491 (1936); Comm. 241*c*.
(46) W. J. de Haas, H. B. G. Casimir and G. J. v. d. Berg. *Physica*, **5**, 225 (1938); Comm. 251*c*.
(47) W. J. de Haas and F. K. du Pré. *Physica*, **5**, 501 (1938); Comm. 253*a*.
(47*a*) W. J. de Haas and F. K. du Pré. *Physica*, **5**, 969 (1938); Comm. 253*c*.
(48) M. H. Hebb and E. M. Purcell. *Journ. Chem. Phys.* **5**, 338 (1937).
(49) W. Heitler and E. Teller. *Proc. Roy. Soc.* **155**, 629 (1936).
(50) W. H. Keesom. *Phys. Z.* **35**, 9 (1934).
(51) H. A. Kramers. *Proc. Kon. Ak. Amst.* **33**, 959 (1930).
(52) K. S. Krishnan and A. Mookherji. *Phys. Rev.* **54**, 533 (1938).
(53) R. de L. Kronig. *Physica*, **5**, 65 (1938).
(54) R. de L. Kronig and C. J. Bouwkamp. *Physica*, **5**, 521 (1938).
(55) R. de L. Kronig. *Phys. Z.* **39**, 823 (1938).
(56) N. Kürti and F. Simon. *Nature*, **133**, 907 (1934).
(57) N. Kürti and F. Simon. *Physica*, **1**, 1107 (1934).
(58) N. Kürti and F. Simon. *Nature*, **135**, 31 (1935).
(59) N. Kürti and F. Simon. *Proc. Roy. Soc.* **149**, 152 (1935).
(60) N. Kürti and F. Simon. *Proc. Roy. Soc.* **151**, 610 (1935).
(61) N. Kürti and F. Simon. *Proc. Roy. Soc.* **152**, 27 (1935).
(62) N. Kürti, B. V. Rollin and F. Simon. *Physica*, **3**, 266 (1936).
(63) N. Kürti, P. Lainé, B. V. Rollin and F. Simon. *C.R.* **202**, 1421 (1936).
(64) N. Kürti, P. Lainé, B. V. Rollin and F. Simon. *C.R.* **202**, 1576 (1936).
(65) N. Kürti, P. Lainé and F. Simon. *C.R.* **204**, 675 (1937).
(66) N. Kürti, P. Lainé and F. Simon. *C.R.* **204**, 754 (1937).
(67) N. Kürti and F. Simon. *Phil. Mag.* **26**, 840 (1938).

(68) N. Kürti and F. Simon. *Phil. Mag.* **26**, 849 (1938).
(69) F. Simon. *Nature*, **135**, 763 (1935).
(70) K. Lichtenecker. *Phys. Z.* **27**, 115 (1926).
(71) H. Lipson and C. A. Beevers. *Proc. Roy. Soc.* **148**, 664 (1935).
(72) L. M. Milne-Thomson and L. J. Comrie. *Standard Four-Figure Mathematical Tables.* Macmillan, 1931.
(73) L. Onsager. *Journ. Am. Chem. Soc.* **58**, 1486 (1936).
(74) A. Siegert. *Physica*, **3**, 85 (1936).
(75) A. Siegert. *Physica*, **4**, 138 (1937).
(76) E. C. Stoner. *Magnetism and Matter.* Methuen, 1934.
(77) J. H. Van Vleck. *Electric and Magnetic Susceptibilities.*
(78) J. H. Van Vleck. *Journ. Chem. Phys.* **5**, 320 (1937).
(79) J. H. Van Vleck. *Journ. Chem. Phys.* **6**, 82 (1938).
(80) I. Waller. *Z. Phys.* **79**, 370 (1932).
(81) I. Waller. *Z. Phys.* **104**, 132 (1936).
(82) E. C. Wiersma. Dissertation, Leiden, 1932.
(83) H. R. Woltjer and H. Kamerlingh Onnes. *Versl. Ak. Amst.* **32**, 772 (1923); Comm. 167*c*.

References to articles published since book was written.

H. B. G. Casimir, W. J. de Haas and D. de Klerk. *Physica*, **6**, 241 (1939); Comm. 256 *a*. (Adiabatic demagnetization of iron-ammonium alum from a number of helium and hydrogen temperatures. Cf. 4.2.)

H. B. G. Casimir, W. J. de Haas and D. de Klerk. *Physica*, **6**, 255 (1939); Comm. 256*b*. (Use of hysteresis for calorimetric purposes. Cf. 4.10.)

H. B. G. Casimir, W. J. de Haas and D. de Klerk. *Physica*, **6**, 365 (1939); Comm. 256*c*. (Adiabatic demagnetization of potassium chromium alum and determination of Stark splitting.)

R. de L. Kronig. *Physica*, **6**, 33 (1939). (Mechanism of paramagnetic relaxation. Cf. 7.4.)

N. Kürti, P. Lainé and F. Simon. *C.R.* **208**, 173 (1939). (Adiabatic demagnetization starting from hydrogen temperatures. Cf. 4.2.)

B. H. Schultz, *Physica*, **6**, 137 (1939); Comm. 253*d*. (New magnetometer. Cf. 2.7.)

E. S. Shire and H. M. Barkla. *Proc. Camb. Phil. Soc.* **35**, 327 (1939). (Heating of iron-ammonium alum by alternating fields at very low temperatures. Cf. 7.5.)

P. Teunissen. Dissertation, Groningen (1939). (Survey of recent work on paramagnetic relaxation.)

J. H. Van Vleck. *Journ. Chem. Phys.* **7**, 61 (1939). (Quenching of orbital magnetism. Cf. 5.2^3.)

INDEX

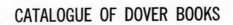

CATALOGUE OF DOVER BOOKS

PHYSICS

General physics

FOUNDATIONS OF PHYSICS, R. B. Lindsay & H. Margenau. Excellent bridge between semi-popular works & technical treatises. A discussion of methods of physical description, construction of theory; valuable for physicist with elementary calculus who is interested in ideas that give meaning to data, tools of modern physics. Contents include symbolism, mathematical equations; space & time foundations of mechanics; probability; physics & continua; electron theory; special & general relativity; quantum mechanics; causality. "Thorough and yet not overdetailed. Unreservedly recommended," NATURE (London). Unabridged, corrected edition. List of recommended readings. 35 illustrations. xi + 537pp. 5⅜ x 8.
S377 Paperbound **$2.75**

FUNDAMENTAL FORMULAS OF PHYSICS, ed. by D. H. Menzel. Highly useful, fully inexpensive reference and study text, ranging from simple to highly sophisticated operations. Mathematics integrated into text—each chapter stands as short textbook of field represented. Vol. 1: Statistics, Physical Constants, Special Theory of Relativity, Hydrodynamics, Aerodynamics, Boundary Value Problems in Math. Physics; Viscosity, Electromagnetic Theory, etc. Vol. 2: Sound, Acoustics, Geometrical Optics, Electron Optics, High-Energy Phenomena, Magnetism, Biophysics, much more. Index. Total of 800pp. 5⅜ x 8.   Vol. 1 S595 Paperbound **$2.00**
Vol. 2 S596 Paperbound **$2.00**

MATHEMATICAL PHYSICS, D. H. Menzel. Thorough one-volume treatment of the mathematical techniques vital for classic mechanics, electromagnetic theory, quantum theory, and relativity. Written by the Harvard Professor of Astrophysics for junior, senior, and graduate courses, it gives clear explanations of all those aspects of function theory, vectors, matrices, dyadics, tensors, partial differential equations, etc., necessary for the understanding of the various physical theories. Electron theory, relativity, and other topics seldom presented appear here in considerable detail. Scores of definitions, conversion factors, dimensional constants, etc. "More detailed than normal for an advanced text . . . excellent set of sections on Dyadics, Matrices, and Tensors," JOURNAL OF THE FRANKLIN INSTITUTE. Index. 193 problems, with answers. x + 412pp. 5⅜ x 8.   S56 Paperbound **$2.00**

THE SCIENTIFIC PAPERS OF J. WILLARD GIBBS. All the published papers of America's outstanding theoretical scientist (except for "Statistical Mechanics" and "Vector Analysis"). Vol I (thermodynamics) contains one of the most brilliant of all 19th-century scientific papers—the 300-page "On the Equilibrium of Heterogeneous Substances," which founded the science of physical chemistry, and clearly stated a number of highly important natural laws for the first time; 8 other papers complete the first volume. Vol II includes 2 papers on dynamics, 8 on vector analysis and multiple algebra, 5 on the electromagnetic theory of light, and 6 miscellaneous papers. Biographical sketch by H. A. Bumstead. Total of xxxvi + 718pp. 5⅜ x 8⅜.
S721 Vol I Paperbound **$2.50**
S722 Vol II Paperbound **$2.00**
The set **$4.50**

BASIC THEORIES OF PHYSICS, Peter Gabriel Bergmann. Two-volume set which presents a critical examination of important topics in the major subdivisions of classical and modern physics. The first volume is concerned with classical mechanics and electrodynamics: mechanics of mass points, analytical mechanics, matter in bulk, electrostatics and magnetostatics, electromagnetic interaction, the field waves, special relativity, and waves. The second volume (Heat and Quanta) contains discussions of the kinetic hypothesis, physics and statistics, stationary ensembles, laws of thermodynamics, early quantum theories, atomic spectra, probability waves, quantization in wave mechanics, approximation methods, and abstract quantum theory. A valuable supplement to any thorough course or text.
Heat and Quanta: Index. 8 figures. x + 300pp. 5⅜ x 8½.   S968 Paperbound **$1.75**
Mechanics and Electrodynamics: Index. 14 figures. vii + 280pp. 5⅜ x 8½.
S969 Paperbound **$1.75**

THEORETICAL PHYSICS, A. S. Kompaneyets. One of the very few thorough studies of the subject in this price range. Provides advanced students with a comprehensive theoretical background. Especially strong on recent experimentation and developments in quantum theory. Contents: Mechanics (Generalized Coordinates, Lagrange's Equation, Collision of Particles, etc.), Electrodynamics (Vector Analysis, Maxwell's equations, Transmission of Signals, Theory of Relativity, etc.), Quantum Mechanics (the Inadequacy of Classical Mechanics, the Wave Equation, Motion in a Central Field, Quantum Theory of Radiation, Quantum Theories of Dispersion and Scattering, etc.), and Statistical Physics (Equilibrium Distribution of Molecules in an Ideal Gas, Boltzmann statistics, Bose and Fermi Distribution, Thermodynamic Quantities, etc.). Revised to 1961. Translated by George Yankovsky, authorized by Kompaneyets. 137 exercises. 56 figures. 529pp. 5⅜ x 8½. S972 Paperbound **$2.50**

ANALYTICAL AND CANONICAL FORMALISM IN PHYSICS, André Mercier. A survey, in one volume, of the variational principles (the key principles—in mathematical form—from which the basic laws of any one branch of physics can be derived) of the several branches of physical theory, together with an examination of the relationships among them. Contents: the Lagrangian Formalism, Lagrangian Densities, Canonical Formalism, Canonical Form of Electrodynamics, Hamiltonian Densities, Transformations, and Canonical Form with Vanishing Jacobian Determinant. Numerous examples and exercises. For advanced students, teachers, etc. 6 figures. Index. viii + 222pp. 5⅜ x 8½.   S1077 Paperbound **$1.75**

Acoustics, optics, electricity and magnetism, electromagnetics, magneto-hydrodynamics

THE THEORY OF SOUND, Lord Rayleigh. Most vibrating systems likely to be encountered in practice can be tackled successfully by the methods set forth by the great Nobel laureate, Lord Rayleigh. Complete coverage of experimental, mathematical aspects of sound theory. Partial contents: Harmonic motions, vibrating systems in general, lateral vibrations of bars, curved plates or shells, applications of Laplace's functions to acoustical problems, fluid friction, plane vortex-sheet, vibrations of solid bodies, etc. This is the first inexpensive edition of this great reference and study work. Bibliography. Historical introduction by R. B. Lindsay. Total of 1040pp. 97 figures. 5⅜ x 8.
S292, S293, Two volume set, paperbound, **$4.70**

THE DYNAMICAL THEORY OF SOUND, H. Lamb. Comprehensive mathematical treatment of the physical aspects of sound, covering the theory of vibrations, the general theory of sound, and the equations of motion of strings, bars, membranes, pipes, and resonators. Includes chapters on plane, spherical, and simple harmonic waves, and the Helmholtz Theory of Audition. Complete and self-contained development for student and specialist; all fundamental differential equations solved completely. Specific mathematical details for such important phenomena as harmonics, normal modes, forced vibrations of strings, theory of reed pipes, etc. Index. Bibliography. 86 diagrams. viii + 307pp. 5⅜ x 8. S655 Paperbound **$1.50**

WAVE PROPAGATION IN PERIODIC STRUCTURES, L. Brillouin. A general method and application to different problems: pure physics, such as scattering of X-rays of crystals, thermal vibration in crystal lattices, electronic motion in metals; and also problems of electrical engineering. Partial contents: elastic waves in 1-dimensional lattices of point masses. Propagation of waves along 1-dimensional lattices. Energy flow. 2 dimensional, 3 dimensional lattices. Mathieu's equation. Matrices and propagation of waves along an electric line. Continuous electric lines. 131 illustrations. Bibliography. Index. xii + 253pp. 5⅜ x 8.
S34 Paperbound **$2.00**

THEORY OF VIBRATIONS, N. W. McLachlan. Based on an exceptionally successful graduate course given at Brown University, this discusses linear systems having 1 degree of freedom, forced vibrations of simple linear systems, vibration of flexible strings, transverse vibrations of bars and tubes, transverse vibration of circular plate, sound waves of finite amplitude, etc. Index. 99 diagrams. 160pp. 5⅜ x 8. S190 Paperbound **$1.35**

LIGHT: PRINCIPLES AND EXPERIMENTS, George S. Monk. Covers theory, experimentation, and research. Intended for students with some background in general physics and elementary calculus. Three main divisions: 1) Eight chapters on geometrical optics—fundamental concepts (the ray and its optical length, Fermat's principle, etc.), laws of image formation, apertures in optical systems, photometry, optical instruments etc.; 2) 9 chapters on physical optics—interference, diffraction, polarization, spectra, the Rayleigh refractometer, the wave theory of light, etc.; 3) 23 instructive experiments based directly on the theoretical text. "Probably the best intermediate textbook on light in the English language. Certainly, it is the best book which includes both geometrical and physical optics," J. Rud Nielson, PHYSICS FORUM. Revised edition. 102 problems and answers. 12 appendices. 6 tables. Index. 270 illustrations. xi +489pp. 5⅜ x 8½. S341 Paperbound **$2.50**

PHOTOMETRY, John W. T. Walsh. The best treatment of both "bench" and "illumination" photometry in English by one of Britain's foremost experts in the field (President of the International Commission on Illumination). Limited to those matters, theoretical and practical, which affect the measurement of light flux, candlepower, illumination, etc., and excludes treatment of the use to which such measurements may be put after they have been made. Chapters on Radiation, The Eye and Vision, Photo-Electric Cells, The Principles of Photometry, The Measurement of Luminous Intensity, Colorimetry, Spectrophotometry, Stellar Photometry, The Photometric Laboratory, etc. Third revised (1958) edition. 281 illustrations. 10 appendices. xxiv + 544pp. 5½ x 9¼. S319 Clothbound **$10.00**

EXPERIMENTAL SPECTROSCOPY, R. A. Sawyer. Clear discussion of prism and grating spectrographs and the techniques of their use in research, with emphasis on those principles and techniques that are fundamental to practically all uses of spectroscopic equipment. Beginning with a brief history of spectroscopy, the author covers such topics as light sources, spectroscopic apparatus, prism spectroscopes and graphs, diffraction grating, the photographic process, determination of wave length, spectral intensity, infrared spectroscopy, spectrochemical analysis, etc. This revised edition contains new material on the production of replica gratings, solar spectroscopy from rockets, new standard of wave length, etc. Index. Bibliography. 111 illustrations. x + 358pp. 5⅜ x 8½. S1045 Paperbound **$2.25**

FUNDAMENTALS OF ELECTRICITY AND MAGNETISM, L. B. Loeb. For students of physics, chemistry, or engineering who want an introduction to electricity and magnetism on a higher level and in more detail than general elementary physics texts provide. Only elementary differential and integral calculus is assumed. Physical laws developed logically, from magnetism to electric currents, Ohm's law, electrolysis, and on to static electricity, induction, etc. Covers an unusual amount of material; one third of book on modern material: solution of wave equation, photoelectric and thermionic effects, etc. Complete statement of the various electrical systems of units and interrelations. 2 Indexes. 75 pages of problems with answers stated. Over 300 figures and diagrams. xix +669pp. 5⅜ x 8. S745 Paperbound **$2.75**

MATHEMATICAL ANALYSIS OF ELECTRICAL AND OPTICAL WAVE-MOTION, Harry Bateman. Written by one of this century's most distinguished mathematical physicists, this is a practical introduction to those developments of Maxwell's electromagnetic theory which are directly connected with the solution of the partial differential equation of wave motion. Methods of solving wave-equation, polar-cylindrical coordinates, diffraction, transformation of coordinates, homogeneous solutions, electromagnetic fields with moving singularities, etc. Index. 168pp. 5⅜ x 8.
S14 Paperbound **$1.75**

PRINCIPLES OF PHYSICAL OPTICS, Ernst Mach. This classical examination of the propagation of light, color, polarization, etc. offers an historical and philosophical treatment that has never been surpassed for breadth and easy readability. Contents: Rectilinear propagation of light. Reflection, refraction. Early knowledge of vision. Dioptrics. Composition of light. Theory of color and dispersion. Periodicity. Theory of interference. Polarization. Mathematical representation of properties of light. Propagation of waves, etc. 279 illustrations, 10 portraits. Appendix. Indexes. 324pp. 5⅜ x 8.
S178 Paperbound **$2.00**

THE THEORY OF OPTICS, Paul Drude. One of finest fundamental texts in physical optics, classic offers thorough coverage, complete mathematical treatment of basic ideas. Includes fullest treatment of application of thermodynamics to optics; sine law in formation of images, transparent crystals, magnetically active substances, velocity of light, apertures, effects depending upon them, polarization, optical instruments, etc. Introduction by A. A. Michelson. Index. 110 illus. 567pp. 5⅜ x 8.
S532 Paperbound **$2.45**

ELECTRICAL THEORY ON THE GIORGI SYSTEM, P. Cornelius. A new clarification of the fundamental concepts of electricity and magnetism, advocating the convenient m.k.s. system of units that is steadily gaining followers in the sciences. Illustrating the use and effectiveness of his terminology with numerous applications to concrete technical problems, the author here expounds the famous Giorgi system of electrical physics. His lucid presentation and well-reasoned, cogent argument for the universal adoption of this system form one of the finest pieces of scientific exposition in recent years. 28 figures. Index. Conversion tables for translating earlier data into modern units. Translated from 3rd Dutch edition by L. J. Jolley. x + 187pp. 5½ x 8¾.
S909 Clothbound **$6.00**

ELECTRIC WAVES: BEING RESEARCHES ON THE PROPAGATION OF ELECTRIC ACTION WITH FINITE VELOCITY THROUGH SPACE, Heinrich Hertz. This classic work brings together the original papers in which Hertz—Helmholtz's protegé and one of the most brilliant figures in 19th-century research—probed the existence of electromagnetic waves and showed experimentally that their velocity equalled that of light, research that helped lay the groundwork for the development of radio, television, telephone, telegraph, and other modern technological marvels. Unabridged republication of original edition. Authorized translation by D. E. Jones. Preface by Lord Kelvin. Index of names. 40 illustrations. xvii + 278pp. 5⅜ x 8½.
S57 Paperbound **$1.75**

PIEZOELECTRICITY: AN INTRODUCTION TO THE THEORY AND APPLICATIONS OF ELECTRO-MECHANICAL PHENOMENA IN CRYSTALS, Walter G. Cady. This is the most complete and systematic coverage of this important field in print—now regarded as something of scientific classic. This republication, revised and corrected by Prof. Cady—one of the foremost contributors in this area—contains a sketch of recent progress and new material on Ferroelectrics. Time Standards, etc. The first 7 chapters deal with fundamental theory of crystal electricity. 5 important chapters cover basic concepts of piezoelectricity, including comparisons of various competing theories in the field. Also discussed: piezoelectric resonators (theory, methods of manufacture, influences of air-gaps, etc.); the piezo oscillator; the properties, history, and observations relating to Rochelle salt; ferroelectric crystals; miscellaneous applications of piezoelectricity; pyroelectricity; etc. "A great work," W. A. Wooster, NATURE. Revised (1963) and corrected edition. New preface by Prof. Cady. 2 Appendices. Indices. Illustrations. 62 tables. Bibliography. Problems. Total of 1 + 822pp. 5⅜ x 8½.
S1094 Vol. I Paperbound **$2.50**
S1095 Vol. II Paperbound **$2.50**
Two volume set Paperbound **$5.00**

MAGNETISM AND VERY LOW TEMPERATURES, H. B. G. Casimir. A basic work in the literature of low temperature physics. Presents a concise survey of fundamental theoretical principles, and also points out promising lines of investigation. Contents: Classical Theory and Experimental Methods, Quantum Theory of Paramagnetism, Experiments on Adiabatic Demagnetization. Theoretical Discussion of Paramagnetism at Very Low Temperatures, Some Experimental Results, Relaxation Phenomena. Index. 89-item bibliography. ix + 95pp. 5⅜ x 8.
S943 Paperbound **$1.25**

SELECTED PAPERS ON NEW TECHNIQUES FOR ENERGY CONVERSION: THERMOELECTRIC METHODS; THERMIONIC; PHOTOVOLTAIC AND ELECTRICAL EFFECTS; FUSION, Edited by Sumner N. Levine. Brings together in one volume the most important papers (1954-1961) in modern energy technology. Included among the 37 papers are general and qualitative descriptions of the field as a whole, indicating promising lines of research. Also: 15 papers on thermoelectric methods, 7 on thermionic, 5 on photovoltaic, 4 on electrochemical effect, and 2 on controlled fusion research. Among the contributors are: Joffe, Maria Telkes, Herold, Herring, Douglas, Jaumot, Post, Austin, Wilson, Pfann, Rappaport, Morehouse, Domenicali, Moss, Bowers, Harman, Von Doenhoef. Preface and introduction by the editor. Bibliographies. xxviii + 451pp. 6⅛ x 9¼.
S37 Paperbound **$3.00**

SUPERFLUIDS: MACROSCOPIC THEORY OF SUPERCONDUCTIVITY, Vol. I, Fritz London. The major work by one of the founders and great theoreticians of modern quantum physics. Consolidates the researches that led to the present understanding of the nature of super-conductivity. Prof. London here reveals that quantum mechanics is operative on the macro-scopic plane as well as the submolecular level. Contents: Properties of Superconductors and Their Thermodynamical Correlation; Electrodynamics of the Pure Superconducting State; Relation between Current and Field; Measurements of the Penetration Depth; Non-Viscous Flow vs. Superconductivity; Micro-waves in Superconductors; Reality of the Domain Structure; and many other related topics. A new epilogue by M. J. Buckingham discusses developments in the field up to 1960. Corrected and expanded edition. An appreciation of the author's life and work by L. W. Nordheim. Biography by Edith London. Bibliography of his publica-tions. 45 figures. 2 Indices. xviii + 173pp. 5⅝ x 8⅜.   S44 Paperbound **$1.45**

SELECTED PAPERS ON PHYSICAL PROCESSES IN IONIZED PLASMAS, Edited by Donald H. Menzel, Director, Harvard College Observatory. 30 important papers relating to the study of highly ionized gases or plasmas selected by a foremost contributor in the field, with the assistance of Dr. L. H. Aller. The essays include 18 on the physical processes in gaseous nebulae, covering problems of radiation and radiative transfer, the Balmer decrement, electron temperatures, spectrophotometry, etc. 10 papers deal with the interpretation of nebular spectra, by Bohm, Van Vleck, Aller, Minkowski, etc. There is also a discussion of the intensities of "forbidden" spectral lines by George Shortley and a paper concern-ing the theory of hydrogenic spectra by Menzel and Pekeris. Other contributors: Goldberg, Hebb, Baker, Bowen, Ufford, Liller, etc. viii + 374pp. 6⅛ x 9¼.   S60 Paperbound **$2.95**

THE ELECTROMAGNETIC FIELD, Max Mason & Warren Weaver. Used constantly by graduate engineers. Vector methods exclusively: detailed treatment of electrostatics, expansion meth-ods, with tables converting any quantity into absolute electromagnetic, absolute electrostatic, practical units. Discrete charges, ponderable bodies, Maxwell field equations, etc. Introduc-tion. Indexes. 416pp. 5⅜ x 8.   S185 Paperbound **$2.00**

THEORY OF ELECTRONS AND ITS APPLICATION TO THE PHENOMENA OF LIGHT AND RADIANT HEAT, H. Lorentz. Lectures delivered at Columbia University by Nobel laureate Lorentz. Unabridged, they form a historical coverage of the theory of free electrons, motion, absorption of heat, Zeeman effect, propagation of light in molecular bodies, inverse Zeeman effect, optical phenomena in moving bodies, etc. 109 pages of notes explain the more advanced sections. Index. 9 figures. 352pp. 5⅜ x 8.   S173 Paperbound **$1.85**

FUNDAMENTAL ELECTROMAGNETIC THEORY, Ronold P. King, Professor Applied Physics, Harvard University. Original and valuable introduction to electromagnetic theory and to circuit theory from the standpoint of electromagnetic theory. Contents: Mathematical Description of Matter—stationary and nonstationary states; Mathematical Description of Space and of Simple Media—Field Equations, Integral Forms of Field Equations, Electromagnetic Force, etc.; Transformation of Field and Force Equations; Electromagnetic Waves in Unbounded Regions; Skin Effect and Internal Impedance—in a solid cylindrical conductor, etc.; and Electrical Circuits—Analytical Foundations, Near-zone and quasi-near zone circuits, Balanced two-wire and four-wire transmission lines. Revised and enlarged version. New preface by the author. 5 appendices (Differential operators: Vector Formulas and Identities, etc.). Problems. Indexes. Bibliography. xvi + 580pp. 5⅜ x 8½.   S1023 Paperbound **$2.75**

Hydrodynamics

A TREATISE ON HYDRODYNAMICS, A. B. Basset. Favorite text on hydrodynamics for 2 genera-tions of physicists, hydrodynamical engineers, oceanographers, ship designers, etc. Clear enough for the beginning student, and thorough source for graduate students and engineers on the work of d'Alembert, Euler, Laplace, Lagrange, Poisson, Green, Clebsch, Stokes, Cauchy, Helmholtz, J. J. Thomson, Love, Hicks, Greenhill, Besant, Lamb, etc. Great amount of docu-mentation on entire theory of classical hydrodynamics. Vol I: theory of motion of frictionless liquids, vortex, and cyclic irrotational motion, etc. 132 exercises. Bibliography. 3 Appendixes. xii + 264pp. Vol II: motion in viscous liquids, harmonic analysis, theory of tides, etc. 112 exercises, Bibliography. 4 Appendixes. xv + 328pp. Two volume set. 5⅜ x 8.
·S724 Vol I Paperbound **$1.75**
S725 Vol II Paperbound **$1.75**
The set **$3.50**

HYDRODYNAMICS, Horace Lamb. Internationally famous complete coverage of standard refer-ence work on dynamics of liquids &. gases. Fundamental theorems, equations, methods, solutions, background, for classical hydrodynamics. Chapters include Equations of Motion, Integration of Equations in Special Gases, Irrotational Motion, Motion of Liquid in 2 Dimen-sions, Motion of Solids through Liquid-Dynamical Theory, Vortex Motion, Tidal Waves, Surface Waves, Waves of Expansion, Viscosity, Rotating Masses of liquids. Excellently planned, ar-ranged; clear, lucid presentation. 6th enlarged, revised edition. Index. Over 900 footnotes, mostly bibliographical. 119 figures. xv + 738pp. 6⅛ x 9¼.   S256 Paperbound **$3.75**

HYDRODYNAMICS, H. Dryden, F. Murnaghan, Harry Bateman. Published by the National Research Council in 1932 this enormous volume offers a complete coverage of classical hydrodynamics. Encyclopedic in quality. Partial contents: physics of fluids, motion, turbulent flow, compressible fluids, motion in 1, 2, 3 dimensions; viscous fluids rotating, laminar motion, resistance of motion through viscous fluid, eddy viscosity, hydraulic flow in channels of various shapes, discharge of gases, flow past obstacles, etc. Bibliography of over 2,900 items. Indexes. 23 figures. 634pp. 5⅜ x 8.　　　　　　　　　　　S303 Paperbound **$2.75**

Mechanics, dynamics, thermodynamics, elasticity

MECHANICS, J. P. Den Hartog. Already a classic among introductory texts, the M.I.T. professor's lively and discursive presentation is equally valuable as a beginner's text, an engineering student's refresher, or a practicing engineer's reference. Emphasis in this highly readable text is on illuminating fundamental principles and showing how they are embodied in a great number of real engineering and design problems: trusses, loaded cables, beams, jacks, hoists, etc. Provides advanced material on relative motion and gyroscopes not usual in introductory texts. "Very thoroughly recommended to all those anxious to improve their real understanding of the principles of mechanics." MECHANICAL WORLD. Index. List of equations. 334 problems, all with answers. Over 550 diagrams and drawings. ix + 462pp. 5⅜ x 8.
S754 Paperbound **$2.00**

THEORETICAL MECHANICS: AN INTRODUCTION TO MATHEMATICAL PHYSICS, J. S. Ames, F. D. Murnaghan. A mathematically rigorous development of theoretical mechanics for the advanced student, with constant practical applications. Used in hundreds of advanced courses. An unusually thorough coverage of gyroscopic and baryscopic material, detailed analyses of the Coriolis acceleration, applications of Lagrange's equations, motion of the double pendulum, Hamilton-Jacobi partial differential equations, group velocity and dispersion, etc. Special relativity is also included. 159 problems. 44 figures. ix + 462pp. 5⅜ x 8.
S461 Paperbound **$2.25**

THEORETICAL MECHANICS: STATICS AND THE DYNAMICS OF A PARTICLE, W. D. MacMillan. Used for over 3 decades as a self-contained and extremely comprehensive advanced undergraduate text in mathematical physics, physics, astronomy, and deeper foundations of engineering. Early sections require only a knowledge of geometry; later, a working knowledge of calculus. Hundreds of basic problems, including projectiles to the moon, escape velocity, harmonic motion, ballistics, falling bodies, transmission of power, stress and strain, elasticity, astronomical problems. 340 practice problems plus many fully worked out examples make it possible to test and extend principles developed in the text. 200 figures. xvii + 430pp. 5⅜ x 8.　　　　　　　　　　　S467 Paperbound **$2.00**

THEORETICAL MECHANICS: THE THEORY OF THE POTENTIAL, W. D. MacMillan. A comprehensive, well balanced presentation of potential theory, serving both as an introduction and a reference work with regard to specific problems, for physicists and mathematicians. No prior knowledge of integral relations is assumed, and all mathematical material is developed as it becomes necessary. Includes: Attraction of Finite Bodies; Newtonian Potential Function; Vector Fields, Green and Gauss Theorems; Attractions of Surfaces and Lines; Surface Distribution of Matter; Two-Layer Surfaces; Spherical Harmonics; Ellipsoidal Harmonics; etc. "The great number of particular cases . . . should make the book valuable to geophysicists and others actively engaged in practical applications of the potential theory," Review of Scientific Instruments. Index. Bibliography. xiii + 469pp. 5⅜ x 8.　　　　S486 Paperbound **$2.25**

THEORETICAL MECHANICS: DYNAMICS OF RIGID BODIES, W. D. MacMillan. Theory of dynamics of a rigid body is developed, using both the geometrical and analytical methods of instruction. Begins with exposition of algebra of vectors, it goes through momentum principles, motion in space, use of differential equations and infinite series to solve more sophisticated dynamics problems. Partial contents: moments of inertia, systems of free particles, motion parallel to a fixed plane, rolling motion, method of periodic solutions, much more. 82 figs. 199 problems. Bibliography. Indexes. xii + 476pp. 5⅜ x 8.　　　S641 Paperbound **$2.00**

MATHEMATICAL FOUNDATIONS OF STATISTICAL MECHANICS, A. I. Khinchin. Offering a precise and rigorous formulation of problems, this book supplies a thorough and up-to-date exposition. It provides analytical tools needed to replace cumbersome concepts, and furnishes for the first time a logical step-by-step introduction to the subject. Partial contents: geometry & kinematics of the phase space, ergodic problem, reduction to theory of probability, application of central limit problem, ideal monatomic gas, foundation of thermo-dynamics, dispersion and distribution of sum functions. Key to notations. Index. viii + 179pp. 5⅜ x 8.
S147 Paperbound **$1.50**

ELEMENTARY PRINCIPLES IN STATISTICAL MECHANICS, J. W. Gibbs. Last work of the great Yale mathematical physicist, still one of the most fundamental treatments available for advanced students and workers in the field. Covers the basic principle of conservation of probability of phase, theory of errors in the calculated phases of a system, the contributions of Clausius, Maxwell, Boltzmann, and Gibbs himself, and much more. Includes valuable comparison of statistical mechanics with thermodynamics: Carnot's cycle, mechanical definitions of entropy, etc. xvi + 208pp. 5⅜ x 8.　　　　　　　　　S707 Paperbound **$1.45**

PRINCIPLES OF MECHANICS AND DYNAMICS, Sir William Thomson (Lord Kelvin) and Peter Guthrie Tait. The principles and theories of fundamental branches of classical physics explained by two of the greatest physicists of all time. A broad survey of mechanics, with material on hydrodynamics, elasticity, potential theory, and what is now standard mechanics. Thorough and detailed coverage, with many examples, derivations, and topics not included in more recent studies. Only a knowledge of calculus is needed to work through this book. Vol. I (Preliminary): Kinematics; Dynamical Laws and Principles; Experience (observation, experimentation, formation of hypotheses, scientific method); Measures and Instruments; Continuous Calculating Machines. Vol. II (Abstract Dynamics): Statics of a Particle—Attraction; Statics of Solids and Fluids. Formerly Titled "Treatise on Natural Philosophy." Unabridged reprint of revised edition. Index. 168 diagrams. Total of xlii + 1035pp. 5⅜ x 8½.
Vol. I: S966 Paperbound **$2.35**
Vol. II: S967 Paperbound **$2.35**
Two volume Set Paperbound **$4.70**

INVESTIGATIONS ON THE THEORY OF THE BROWNIAN MOVEMENT, Albert Einstein. Reprints from rare European journals. 5 basic papers, including the Elementary Theory of the Brownian Movement, written at the request of Lorentz to provide a simple explanation. Translated by A. D. Cowper. Annotated, edited by R. Fürth. 33pp. of notes elucidate, give history of previous investigations. Author, subject indexes. 62 footnotes. 124pp. 5⅜ x 8.
S304 Paperbound **$1.25**

MECHANICS VIA THE CALCULUS, P. W. Norris, W. S. Legge. Covers almost everything, from linear motion to vector analysis: equations determining motion, linear methods, compounding of simple harmonic motions, Newton's laws of motion, Hooke's law, the simple pendulum, motion of a particle in 1 plane, centers of gravity, virtual work, friction, kinetic energy of rotating bodies, equilibrium of strings, hydrostatics, sheering stresses, elasticity, etc. 550 problems. 3rd revised edition. xii + 367pp. 6 x 9. S207 Clothbound **$4.95**

THE DYNAMICS OF PARTICLES AND OF RIGID, ELASTIC, AND FLUID BODIES; BEING LECTURES ON MATHEMATICAL PHYSICS, A. G. Webster. The reissuing of this classic fills the need for a comprehensive work on dynamics. A wide range of topics is covered in unusually great depth, applying ordinary and partial differential equations. Part I considers laws of motion and methods applicable to systems of all sorts; oscillation, resonance, cyclic systems, etc. Part 2 is a detailed study of the dynamics of rigid bodies. Part 3 introduces the theory of potential; stress and strain, Newtonian potential functions, gyrostatics, wave and vortex motion, etc. Further contents: Kinematics of a point; Lagrange's equations; Hamilton's principle; Systems of vectors; Statics and dynamics of deformable bodies; much more, not easily found together in one volume. Unabridged reprinting of 2nd edition. 20 pages of notes on differential equations and the higher analysis. 203 illustrations. Selected bibliography. Index. xi + 588pp. 5⅜ x 8. S522 Paperbound **$2.45**

A TREATISE ON DYNAMICS OF A PARTICLE, E. J. Routh. Elementary text on dynamics for beginning mathematics or physics student. Unusually detailed treatment from elementary definitions to motion in 3 dimensions, emphasizing concrete aspects. Much unique material important in recent applications. Covers impulsive forces, rectilinear and constrained motion in 2 dimensions, harmonic and parabolic motion, degrees of freedom, closed orbits, the conical pendulum, the principle of least action, Jacobi's method, and much more. Index. 559 problems, many fully worked out, incorporated into text. xiii + 418pp. 5⅜ x 8.
S696 Paperbound **$2.25**

DYNAMICS OF A SYSTEM OF RIGID BODIES (Elementary Section), E. J. Routh. Revised 7th edition of this standard reference. This volume covers the dynamical principles of the subject, and its more elementary applications: finding moments of inertia by integration, foci of inertia, d'Alembert's principle, impulsive forces, motion in 2 and 3 dimensions, Lagrange's equations, relative indicatrix, Euler's theorem, large tautochronous motions, etc. Index. 55 figures. Scores of problems. xv + 443pp. 5⅜ x 8. S664 Paperbound **$2.50**

DYNAMICS OF A SYSTEM OF RIGID BODIES (Advanced Section), E. J. Routh. Revised 6th edition of a classic reference aid. Much of its material remains unique. Partial contents: moving axes, relative motion, oscillations about equilibrium, motion. Motion of a body under no forces, any forces. Nature of motion given by linear equations and conditions of stability. Free, forced vibrations, constants of integration, calculus of finite differences, variations, precession and nutation, motion of the moon, motion of string, chain, membranes. 64 figures. 498pp. 5⅜ x 8. S229 Paperbound **$2.45**

DYNAMICAL THEORY OF GASES, James Jeans. Divided into mathematical and physical chapters for the convenience of those not expert in mathematics, this volume discusses the mathematical theory of gas in a steady state, thermodynamics, Boltzmann and Maxwell, kinetic theory, quantum theory, exponentials, etc. 4th enlarged edition, with new material on quantum theory, quantum dynamics, etc. Indexes. 28 figures. 444pp. 6⅛ x 9¼.
S136 Paperbound **$2.65**

THE THEORY OF HEAT RADIATION, Max Planck. A pioneering work in thermodynamics, providing basis for most later work, Nobel laureate Planck writes on Deductions from Electrodynamics and Thermodynamics, Entropy and Probability, Irreversible Radiation Processes, etc. Starts with simple experimental laws of optics, advances to problems of spectral distribution of energy and irreversibility. Bibliography. 7 illustrations, xiv + 224pp. 5⅜ x 8.
S546 Paperbound **$1.75**

FOUNDATIONS OF POTENTIAL THEORY, O. D. Kellogg. Based on courses given at Harvard this is suitable for both advanced and beginning mathematicians. Proofs are rigorous, and much material not generally avaliable elsewhere is included. Partial contents: forces of gravity, fields of force, divergence theorem, properties of Newtonian potentials at points of free space, potentials as solutions of Laplace's equations, harmonic functions, electrostatics, electric images, logarithmic potential, etc. One of Grundlehren Series. ix + 384pp. 5⅜ x 8.
S144 Paperbound **$1.98**

THERMODYNAMICS, Enrico Fermi. Unabridged reproduction of 1937 edition. Elementary in treatment; remarkable for clarity, organization. Requires no knowledge of advanced math beyond calculus, only familiarity with fundamentals of thermometry, calorimetry. Partial Contents: Thermodynamic systems; First & Second laws of thermodynamics; Entropy; Thermodynamic potentials: phase rule, reversible electric cell; Gaseous reactions: van't Hoff reaction box, principle of LeChatelier; Thermodynamics of dilute solutions: osmotic & vapor pressures, boiling & freezing points; Entropy constant. Index. 25 problems. 24 illustrations. x + 160pp. 5⅜ x 8.
S361 Paperbound **$1.75**

THE THERMODYNAMICS OF ELECTRICAL PHENOMENA IN METALS and A CONDENSED COLLECTION OF THERMODYNAMIC FORMULAS, P. W. Bridgman. Major work by the Nobel Prizewinner: stimulating conceptual introduction to aspects of the electron theory of metals, giving an intuitive understanding of fundamental relationships concealed by the formal systems of Onsager and others. Elementary mathematical formulations show clearly the fundamental thermodynamical relationships of the electric field, and a complete phenomenological theory of metals is created. This is the work in which Bridgman announced his famous "thermomotive force" and his distinction between "driving" and "working" electromotive force. We have added in this Dover edition the author's long unavailable tables of thermodynamic formulas, extremely valuable for the speed of reference they allow. Two works bound as one. Index. 33 figures. Bibliography. xviii + 256pp. 5⅜ x 8. S723 Paperbound **$1.65**

TREATISE ON THERMODYNAMICS, Max Planck. Based on Planck's original papers this offers a uniform point of view for the entire field and has been used as an introduction for students who have studied elementary chemistry, physics, and calculus. Rejecting the earlier approaches of Helmholtz and Maxwell, the author makes no assumptions regarding the nature of heat, but begins with a few empirical facts, and from these deduces new physical and chemical laws. 3rd English edition of this standard text by a Nobel laureate. xvi + 297pp. 5⅜ x 8.
S219 Paperbound **$1.75**

THE MATHEMATICAL THEORY OF ELASTICITY, A. E. H. Love. A wealth of practical illustration combined with thorough discussion of fundamentals—theory, application, special problems and solutions. Partial Contents: Analysis of Strain & Stress, Elasticity of Solid Bodies, Elasticity of Crystals, Vibration of Spheres, Cylinders, Propagation of Waves in Elastic Solid Media, Torsion, Theory of Continuous Beams, Plates. Rigorous treatment of Volterra's theory of dislocations, 2-dimensional elastic systems, other topics of modern interest. "For years the standard treatise on elasticity," AMERICAN MATHEMATICAL MONTHLY. 4th revised edition. Index. 76 figures. xviii + 643pp. 6⅛ x 9¼. S174 Paperbound **$3.25**

STRESS WAVES IN SOLIDS, H. Kolsky, Professor of Applied Physics, Brown University. The most readable survey of the theoretical core of current knowledge about the propagation of waves in solids, fully correlated with experimental research. Contents: Part I—Elastic Waves: propagation in an extended plastic medium, propagation in bounded elastic media, experimental investigations with elastic materials. Part II—Stress Waves in Imperfectly Elastic Media: internal friction, experimental investigations of dynamic elastic properties, plastic waves and shock waves, fractures produced by stress waves. List of symbols. Appendix. Supplemented bibliography. 3 full-page plates. 46 figures. x + 213pp. 5⅜ x 8½.
S1098 Paperbound **$1.75**

Relativity, quantum theory, atomic and nuclear physics

SPACE TIME MATTER, Hermann Weyl. "The standard treatise on the general theory of relativity" (Nature), written by a world-renowned scientist, provides a deep clear discussion of the logical coherence of the general theory, with introduction to all the mathematical tools needed: Maxwell, analytical geometry, non-Euclidean geometry, tensor calculus, etc. Basis is classical space-time, before absorption of relativity. Partial contents: Euclidean space, mathematical form, metrical continuum, relativity of time and space, general theory. 15 diagrams. Bibliography. New preface for this edition. xviii + 330pp. 5⅜ x 8.
S267 Paperbound **$2.00**

ATOMIC SPECTRA AND ATOMIC STRUCTURE, G. Herzberg. Excellent general survey for chemists, physicists specializing in other fields. Partial contents: simplest line spectra and elements of atomic theory, building-up principle and periodic system of elements, hyperfine structure of spectral lines, some experiments and applications. Bibliography. 80 figures. Index. xii + 257pp. 5⅜ x 8.
S115 Paperbound **$2.00**

THE PRINCIPLE OF RELATIVITY, A. Einstein, H. Lorentz, H. Minkowski, H. Weyl. These are the 11 basic papers that founded the general and special theories of relativity, all translated into English. Two papers by Lorentz on the Michelson experiment, electromagnetic phenomena. Minkowski's SPACE & TIME, and Weyl's GRAVITATION & ELECTRICITY. 7 epochmaking papers by Einstein: ELECTROMAGNETICS OF MOVING BODIES, INFLUENCE OF GRAVITATION IN PROPAGATION OF LIGHT, COSMOLOGICAL CONSIDERATIONS, GENERAL THEORY, and 3 others. 7 diagrams. Special notes by A. Sommerfeld. 224pp. 5⅜ x 8.
S81 Paperbound **$1.75**

EINSTEIN'S THEORY OF RELATIVITY, Max Born. Revised edition prepared with the collaboration of Gunther Leibfried and Walter Biem. Steering a middle course between superficial popularizations and complex analyses, a Nobel laureate explains Einstein's theories clearly and with special insight. Easily followed by the layman with a knowledge of high school mathematics, the book has been thoroughly revised and extended to modernize those sections of the well-known original edition which are now out of date. After a comprehensive review of classical physics, Born's discussion of special and general theories of relativity covers such topics as simultaneity, kinematics, Einstein's mechanics and dynamics, relativity of arbitrary motions, the geometry of curved surfaces, the space-time continuum, and many others. Index. Illustrations, vii + 376pp. 5⅜ x 8.
S769 Paperbound **$2.00**

ATOMS, MOLECULES AND QUANTA, Arthur E. Ruark and Harold C. Urey. Revised (1963) and corrected edition of a work that has been a favorite with physics students and teachers for more than 30 years. No other work offers the same combination of atomic structure and molecular physics and of experiment and theory. The first 14 chapters deal with the origins and major experimental data of quantum theory and with the development of conceptions of atomic and molecular structure prior to the new mechanics. These sections provide a thorough introduction to atomic and molecular theory, and are presented lucidly and as simply as possible. The six subsequent chapters are devoted to the laws and basic ideas of quantum mechanics: Wave Mechanics, Hydrogenic Atoms in Wave Mechanics, Matrix Mechanics, General Theory of Quantum Dynamics, etc. For advanced college and graduate students in physics. Revised, corrected republication of original edition, with supplementary notes by the authors. New preface by the authors. 9 appendices. General reference list. Indices. 228 figures. 71 tables. Bibliographical material in notes, etc. Total of xxiii + 810pp. 5⅜ x 8⅜.
S1106 Vol. I Paperbound **$2.50**
S1107 Vol. II Paperbound **$2.50**
Two volume set Paperbound **$5.00**

WAVE MECHANICS AND ITS APPLICATIONS, N. F. Mott and I. N. Sneddon. A comprehensive introduction to the theory of quantum mechanics; not a rigorous mathematical exposition it progresses, instead, in accordance with the physical problems considered. Many topics difficult to find at the elementary level are discussed in this book. Includes such matters as: the wave nature of matter, the wave equation of Schrödinger, the concept of stationary states, properties of the wave functions, effect of a magnetic field on the energy levels of atoms, electronic spin, two-body problem, theory of solids, cohesive forces in ionic crystals, collision problems, interaction of radiation with matter, relativistic quantum mechanics, etc. All are treated both physically and mathematically. 68 illustrations. 11 tables. Indexes. xii + 393pp. 5⅜ x 8½.
S1070 Paperbound **$2.25**

BASIC METHODS IN TRANSFER PROBLEMS, V. Kourganoff, Professor of Astrophysics, U. of Paris. A coherent digest of all the known methods which can be used for approximate or exact solutions of transfer problems. All methods demonstrated on one particular problem —Milne's problem for a plane parallel medium. Three main sections: fundamental concepts (the radiation field and its interaction with matter, the absorption and emission coefficients, etc.); different methods by which transfer problems can be attacked; and a more general problem—the non-grey case of Milne's problem. Much new material, drawing upon declassified atomic energy reports and data from the USSR. Entirely understandable to the student with a reasonable knowledge of analysis. Unabridged, revised reprinting. New preface by the author. Index. Bibliography. 2 appendices. xv + 281pp. 5⅜ x 8½.
S1074 Paperbound **$2.00**

PRINCIPLES OF QUANTUM MECHANICS, W. V. Houston. Enables student with working knowledge of elementary mathematical physics to develop facility in use of quantum mechanics, understand published work in field. Formulates quantum mechanics in terms of Schroedinger's wave mechanics. Studies evidence for quantum theory, for inadequacy of classical mechanics, 2 postulates of quantum mechanics; numerous important, fruitful applications of quantum mechanics in spectroscopy, collision problems, electrons in solids; other topics. "One of the most rewarding features . . . is the interlacing of problems with text," Amer. J. of Physics. Corrected edition. 21 illus. Index. 296pp. 5⅜ x 8. S524 Paperbound **$2.00**

PHYSICAL PRINCIPLES OF THE QUANTUM THEORY, Werner Heisenberg. A Nobel laureate discusses quantum theory; Heisenberg's own work, Compton, Schroedinger, Wilson, Einstein, many others. Written for physicists, chemists who are not specialists in quantum theory, only elementary formulae are considered in the text; there is a mathematical appendix for specialists. Profound without sacrifice of clarity. Translated by C. Eckart, F. Hoyt. 18 figures. 192pp. 5⅜ x 8.
S113 Paperbound **$1.25**

PHYSICS, HISTORIES AND CLASSICS

A HISTORY OF PHYSICS: IN ITS ELEMENTARY BRANCHES (THROUGH 1925), INCLUDING THE EVOLUTION OF PHYSICAL LABORATORIES, Florian Cajori. Revised and enlarged edition. The only first-rate brief history of physics. Still the best entry for a student or teacher into the antecedents of modern theories of physics. A clear, non-mathematical, handy reference work which traces in critical fashion the developments of ideas, theories, techniques, and apparatus from the Greeks to the 1920's. Within each period he analyzes the basic topics of mechanics, light, electricity and magnetism, sound, atomic theory and structure of matter, radioactivity, etc. A chapter on modern research: Curie, Kelvin, Planck's quantum theory, thermodynamics, Fitzgerald and Lorentz, special and general relativity, J. J. Thomson's model of an atom, Bohr's discoveries and later results, wave mechanics, and many other matters. Much bibliographic detail in footnotes. Index. 16 figures. xv + 424pp. 5⅜ x 8.   T970 Paperbound **$2.00**

A HISTORY OF THE MATHEMATICAL THEORIES OF ATTRACTION AND THE FIGURE OF THE EARTH: FROM THE TIME OF NEWTON TO THAT OF LAPLACE, I. Todhunter. A technical and detailed review of the theories concerning the shape of the earth and its gravitational pull, from the earliest investigations in the seventeenth century up to the middle of the nineteenth. Some of the greatest mathematicians and scientists in history applied themselves to these questions: Newton ("Principia Mathematica"), Huygens, Maupertuis, Simpson, d'Alembert, etc. Others discussed are Poisson, Gauss, Plana, Lagrange, Boit, and many more. Particular emphasis is placed on the theories of Laplace and Legendre, several chapters being devoted to Laplace's "Mécanique Céleste" and his memoirs, and several others to the memoirs of Legendre. Important to historians of science and mathematics and to the specialist who desires background information in the field. 2 volumes bound as 1. Index. xxxvi + 984pp. 5⅜ x 8.
S148 Clothbound **$7.50**

OPTICKS, Sir Isaac Newton. In its discussions of light, reflection, color, refraction, theories of wave and corpuscular theories of light, this work is packed with scores of insights and discoveries. In its precise and practical discussion of construction of optical apparatus, contemporary understandings of phenomena it is truly fascinating to modern physicists, astronomers, mathematicians. Foreword by Albert Einstein. Preface by I. B. Cohen of Harvard University. 7 pages of portraits, facsimile pages, letters, etc. cxvi + 414pp. 5⅜ x 8.
S205 Paperbound **$2.25**

TREATISE ON LIGHT, Christiaan Huygens. The famous original formulation of the wave theory of light, this readable book is one of the two decisive and definitive works in the field of light (Newton's "Optics" is the other). A scientific giant whose researches ranged over mathematics, astronomy, and physics, Huygens, in this historic work, covers such topics as rays propagated in straight lines, reflection and refraction, the spreading and velocity of light, the nature of opaque bodies, the non-spherical nature of light in the atmosphere, properties of Iceland Crystal, and other related matters. Unabridged republication of original (1912) English edition. Translated and introduced by Silvanus P. Thompson. 52 illustrations. xii + 129pp. 5⅜ x 8.
S179 Paperbound **$1.50**

FARADAY'S EXPERIMENTAL RESEARCHES IN ELECTRICITY. Faraday's historic series of papers containing the fruits of years of original experimentation in electrical theory and electrochemistry. Covers his findings in a variety of areas: Induction of electric currents, Evolution of electricity from magnetism, New electrical state or condition of matter, Explication of Arago's magnetic phenomena, New law of electric conduction, Electro-chemical decomposition, Electricity of the Voltaic Pile, Static Induction, Nature of the electric force or forces, Nature of electric current, The character and direction of the electric force of the Gymnotus, Magneto-electric spark, The magnetization of light and the illumination of magnetic lines of force, The possible relation of gravity to electricity, Sub-terraneous electrotelegraph wires, Some points of magnetic philosophy, The diamagnetic conditions of flame and gases, and many other matters. Complete and unabridged republication. 3 vols. bound as 2. Originally reprinted from the Philosophical Transactions of 1831-8. Indices. Illustrations. Total of 1463pp. 5⅜ x 8.   S783-4, Clothbound **$17.50** (tentative)

REFLECTIONS ON THE MOTIVE POWER OF FIRE, Sadi Carnot, and other papers on the 2nd law of thermodynamics by E. Clapeyron and R. Clausius. Carnot's "Reflections" laid the groundwork of modern thermodynamics. Its non-technical, mostly verbal statements examine the relations between heat and the work done by heat in engines, establishing conditions for the economical working of these engines. The papers by Clapeyron and Clausius here reprinted added further refinements to Carnot's work, and led to its final acceptance by physicists. Selections from posthumous manuscripts of Carnot are also included. All papers in English. New introduction by E. Mendoza. 12 illustrations. xxii + 152pp. 5⅜ x 8.

S661 Paperbound **$1.50**

DIALOGUES CONCERNING TWO NEW SCIENCES, Galileo Galilei. This classic of experimental science, mechanics, engineering, is as enjoyable as it is important. A great historical document giving insights into one of the world's most original thinkers, it is based on 30 years' experimentation. It offers a lively exposition of dynamics, elasticity, sound, ballistics, strength of materials, the scientific method. "Superior to everything else of mine," Galileo. Trans. by H. Crew, A. Salvio. 126 diagrams. Index. xxi + 288pp. 5⅜ x 8.
S99 Paperbound **$1.75**

TREATISE ON ELECTRICITY AND MAGNETISM, James Clerk Maxwell. For more than 80 years a seemingly inexhaustible source of leads for physicists, mathematicians, engineers. Total of 1082pp. on such topics as Measurement of Quantities, Electrostatics, Elementary Mathematical Theory of Electricity, Electrical Work and Energy in a System of Conductors, General Theorems, Theory of Electrical Images, Electrolysis, Conduction, Polarization, Dielectrics, Resistance, etc. "The greatest mathematical physicist since Newton," Sir James Jeans. 3rd edition. 107 figures, 21 plates. 1082pp. 5⅜ x 8.   S636-7, 2 volume set, paperbound **$4.00**

A HISTORY OF THE THEORY OF ELASTICITY AND THE STRENGTH OF MATERIALS, I. Todhunter and K. Pearson. For over 60 years a basic reference, unsurpassed in scope or authority. Both a history of the mathematical theory of elasticity, from Galileo, Hooke, and Mariotte to Saint Venant, Kirchhoff, Clebsch, and Lord Kelvin and a detailed presentation of every important mathematical contribution during this period. Presents proofs of thousands of theorems and laws, summarizes every relevant treatise, many unavailable elsewhere. Practically a book apiece is devoted to modern founders: Saint Venant, Lamé, Boussinesq, Rankine, Lord Kelvin, F. Neumann, Kirchhoff, Clebsch. Hundreds of pages of technical and physical treatises on specific applications of elasticity to particular materials. Indispensable for the mathematician, physicist, or engineer working with elasticity. Unabridged, corrected reprint of original 3-volume 1886-1893 edition. Three volume set. Two indexes. Appendix to Vol. I. Total of 2344pp. 5⅜ x 8⅜.   S914–916 The set, Clothbound **$15.00**

DE MAGNETE, William Gilbert. This classic work on magnetism founded a new science. Gilbert was the first to use the word "electricity", to recognize mass as distinct from weight, to discover the effect of heat on magnetic bodies; invent an electroscope, differentiate between static electricity and magnetism, conceive of the earth as a magnet. Written by the first great experimental scientist, this lively work is valuable not only as an historical landmark, but as the delightfully easy to follow record of a perpetually searching, ingenious mind. Translated by P. F. Mottelay. 25-page biographical memoir. 90 figures. lix +368pp. 5⅜ x 8.   S470 Paperbound **$2.00**

ASTRONOMY

THE INTERNAL CONSTITUTION OF THE STARS, Sir A. S. Eddington. Influence of this has been enormous; first detailed exposition of theory of radiative equilibrium for stellar interiors, of all available evidence for existence of diffuse matter in interstellar space. Studies quantum theory, polytropic gas spheres, mass-luminosity relations, variable stars, etc. Discussions of equations paralleled with informal exposition of intimate relationship of astrophysics with great discoveries in atomic physics, radiation. Introduction. Appendix. Index. 421pp. 5⅜ x 8.   S563 Paperbound **$2.75**

PLANETARY THEORY, E. W. Brown and C. A. Shook. Provides a clear presentation of basic methods for calculating planetary orbits for today's astronomer. Begins with a careful exposition of specialized mathematical topics essential for handling perturbation theory and then goes on to indicate how most of the previous methods reduce ultimately to two general calculation methods: obtaining expressions either for the coordinates of planetary positions or for the elements which determine the perturbed paths. An example of each is given and worked in detail. Corrected edition. Preface. Appendix. Index. xii + 302pp. 5⅜ x 8½.   S1133 Paperbound **$2.25**

CANON OF ECLIPSES (CANON DER FINSTERNISSE), Prof. Theodor Ritter von Oppolzer. Since its original publication in 1887, this has been the standard reference and the most extensive single volume of data on the calculation of solar and lunar eclipses, past and future. A comprehensive introduction gives a full explanation of the use of the tables for the calculations of the exact dates of eclipses, etc. Data furnished for the calculation of 8,000 solar and 5,200 lunar eclipses, going back as far as 1200 B.C. and giving predictions up to the year 2161. Information is also given for partial and ring eclipses. All calculations based on Universal (Greenwich) Time. An unsurpassed reference work for astronomers, scientists engaged in space research and developments, historians, etc. Unabridged republication, with corrections. Preface to this edition by Donald Menzel and Owen Gingerich of the Harvard College Observatory. Translated by Owen Gingerich. 160 charts. lxx + 538pp. 8⅜ x 11¼.   S114 Clothbound **$10.00**

THEORY OF THE MOTION OF THE HEAVENLY BODIES MOVING ABOUT THE SUN IN CONIC SECTIONS, Karl Friedrich Gauss. A landmark of theoretical astronomy by the great German scientist. Still authoritative and invaluable to the practicing astronomer. Part I develops the relations between the quantities on which the motion about the sun of the heavenly bodies depends—relations pertaining simply to position in the orbit, simply to position in space, between several places in orbit, and between several places in space. The calculation methods of Part II based on the groundwork of Part I include: determination of an orbit from 3 complete observations, from 4 observations (of which only two are complete), determination of an orbit satisfying as nearly as possible any number of observations whatever, and determination of orbits, taking into account the perturbations. Translation of "Theoria Motus" and with an appendix by C. H. Davis. Unabridged republication. Appendices and tables. 13 figures. xviii + 376pp. 6½ x 9¼.   S1056 Paperbound **$2.95**

THE GALACTIC NOVAE, C. Payne-Gaposchkin, Prof. of Astronomy, Harvard Univ. A work that will be the standard reference source for years to come. Gathers together all the pertinent data, results recorded by countless observers of galactic novae over the centuries, in order to formulate a valid starting point for an interpretation of the nova process. Covers information and statistics on known novae, their variations in luminosity, distribution in the sky, spectral changes, etc.; symbiotic novae; frequently-recurring variables of the U Geminorum and Z Camelopardis class; supernovae; comparison of spectral changes; theories and interpretations of these phenomena, etc. "A comprehensive summary of everything that is now known about these stars," SCIENCE. Bibliographical references. Preface. Indices. 49 figures. 6 plates. 101 tables. x + 336pp. 5⅜ x 8⅜. **S1170 Paperbound $2.45**

BINARY STARS, R. G. Aitken. Still the definitive work in the field of double star astronomy. Written by the director of the Lick Observatory (considered the father of the modern study of binary star systems), this book sums up the results of 40 years of experience in the field, plus the work of centuries of research. Includes historical survey of major discoveries and contributions of the past, observational methods for visual binary stars, the radial velocity of a star (by Dr. J. H. Moore), eclipsing binary stars, known orbits of binary stars, some binary systems of special interest, the origin of binary stars. Much information on methods of spectrum analysis, orbit plotting, use of the telescope, and other practical matters. Useful for classroom study and advanced hobbyists, etc. Revised edition, corrected and with additional notes by Prof. J. T. Kent. New preface. 50 tables, 13 figures, 4 full-page plates. Bibliographies. Appendix. Indices. xii + 309pp. 5⅜ x 8½. **S1102 Paperbound $2.00**

THE NATURE OF COMETS, N. B. Richter. An authority on comets presents a concise, but thorough survey of the state of our present-day knowledge of comets and cometary activity. Based on over 20 years of research, this is a middle-level account that even the layman can appreciate, providing a fund of information on historical theories (from 1700 to the present); statistical research on total number of comets, orbital forms, perturbations caused by Jupiter, comet groups, etc.; the structure of a comet; comets as processes of cosmic decay; origin and formation of comets; etc. Also: a lengthy introduction on modern theories by Dr. R. A. Lyttleton, much technical data and observational material of specific comets, supplementary tables, and the like. Revised (1963) edition. Translated and revised by Arthur Beer. 69 illustrations, including 54 photographs of comets, tails, spectra. 41 tables. Bibliography. Index. xli + 221pp. **S1111 Clothbound $10.00**

CELESTIAL OBJECTS FOR COMMON TELESCOPES, Rev. T. W. Webb. Classic handbook for the use and pleasure of the amateur astronomer. Of inestimable aid in locating and identifying thousands of celestial objects. Vol. I, The Solar System: discussions of the principle and operation of the telescope, procedures of observations and telescope-photography, spectroscopy, etc., precise location information of sun, moon, planets, meteors. Vol. II, The Stars: alphabetical listing of constellations, information on double stars, clusters, stars with unusual spectra, variables, and nebulae, etc. Nearly 4,000 objects noted. Edited and extensively revised by Margaret W. Mayall, director of the American Assn. of Variable Star Observers. New Index by Mrs. Mayall giving the location of all objects mentioned in the text for Epoch 2000. New Precession Table added. New appendices on the planetary satellites, constellation names and abbreviations, and solar system data. Total of 46 illustrations. Total of xxxix + 606pp. 5⅜ x 8.
Vol. I: T917 Paperbound **$2.25**
Vol. II: T918 Paperbound **$2.25**
Two Volume Set Paperbound **$4.50**

ASTRONOMY AND COSMOGONY, Sir James Jeans. A modern classic which is still of enormous value to everyone in astronomy, etc., this is Jean's last and most famous exposition. The summation of a lifetime's devotion to science, it presents his final conclusions on a host of problems ranging over the whole of descriptive astronomy, astrophysics, stellar dynamics, and cosmology. Contents: The Light from the Stars, Gaseous Stars, the Source of Stellar Energy, Liquid Stars, The Evolution of the Stars, The Configuration of Rotating Masses, The Evolution of Binary Systems, The Ages of the Stars, The Great Nebulae, The Galactic Systems, Variable Stars, etc. New preface by L. Motz, Columbia U. 16 full-page photographic illustrations. xv + 428pp. 5⅝ x 8⅜. **S923 Paperbound $2.45**

ASTRONOMY OF STELLAR ENERGY AND DECAY, Martin Johnson. Middle level treatment of astronomy as interpreted by modern atomic physics. Part One is non-technical, examines physical properties, source of energy, spectroscopy, fluctuating stars, various models and theories, etc. Part Two parallels these topics, providing their mathematical foundation. "Clear, concise, and readily understandable," American Library Assoc. Bibliography. 3 indexes. 29 illustrations. 216pp. 5⅜ x 8. **S537 Paperbound $1.50**

MATHEMATICAL THEORIES OF PLANETARY MOTIONS, Otto Dziobek. Translated by Mark W. Harrington and William J. Hussey. Lucid account of the principles of mathematical astronomy. It examines that part of celestial mechanics which deals with the motions of heavenly bodies considered as material points. Contents: Solution of the Problem of Two Bodies; Formation of the General Integrals for Problem of n Bodies . . . including discussions of elliptic, parabolic, and hyperbolic orbits, the solution of Kepler's equation, etc.; and sections headed The General Properties of the Integrals and The Theory of Perturbations . . . which deals with the theory of absolute perturbations, analytical development of the perturbing function, the variation of the elements, the secular variation of the mean longitude, etc. vi + 294pp. 5⅜ x 8½. **S129 Paperbound $2.00**

A COMPENDIUM OF SPHERICAL ASTRONOMY, S. Newcomb. Long a standard collection of basic methods and formulas most useful to the working astronomer, and clear full text for students. Includes the most important common approximations; 40 pages on the method of least squares; general theory of spherical coordinates; parallax; aberration; astronomical refraction; theory of precession; proper motion of the stars; methods of deriving positions of stars; and much more. Index. 9 Appendices of tables, formulas, etc. 36 figures. xviii + 444pp. 5⅜ x 8.
S690 Paperbound **$2.25**

PRINCIPLES OF STELLAR DYNAMICS, S. Chandrasekhar. A leading astrophysicist here presents the theory of stellar dynamics as a branch of classical dynamics, clarifying the fundamental issues and the underlying motivations of the theory. He analyzes the effects of stellar encounters in terms of the classical 2-body problem, and investigates problems centering about Liouville's theorem and the solutions of the equations of continuity. This edition also includes 4 important papers by the author published since "Stellar Dynamics," and equally indispensable for all workers in the field: "New Methods in Stellar Dynamics" and "Dynamical Friction," Parts I, II, and III. Index. 3 Appendixes. Bibliography. 50 illustrations. x + 313pp. 5⅜ x8.
S659 Paperbound **$2.25**

AN INTRODUCTION TO THE STUDY OF STELLAR STRUCTURE, Subrahmanyan Chandrasekhar. Outstanding treatise on stellar dynamics by one of world's greatest astrophysicists. Uses classical & modern math methods to examine relationship between loss of energy, the mass, and radius of stars in a steady state. Discusses thermodynamic laws from Carathéodory's axiomatic standpoint; adiabatic, polytropic laws; work of Ritter, Emden, Kelvin, others; Stroemgren envelopes as starter for theory of gaseous stars; Gibbs statistical mechanics (quantum); degenerate stellar configuration & theory of white dwarfs, etc. "Highest level of scientific merit," BULLETIN, AMER. MATH. SOC. Bibliography. Appendixes. Index. 33 figures. 509pp. 5⅜ x 8.
S413 Paperbound **$2.75**

STATISTICAL ASTRONOMY, Robert J. Trumpler and Harold F. Weaver, University of California. Standard introduction to the principles and techniques of statistical astronomy, a field of rapidly growing importance in this space age. An extensive section, "Elements of Statistical Theory," provides the astronomer with the tools for solving problems of descriptive astronomy, observational errors, constitution of extra-galactic nebulae, etc. Procedures used in statistical astronomy are related to basic mathematical principles of statistics such as univariate distribution, integral equations, general theory of samples, etc. Other sections deal with: Statistical Description of the Galactic System; Stellar Motions in the Vicinity of the Sun; Luminosity—Spectral Type Distribution; Space Distribution of Stars; and Galactic Rotation. List of symbols. Appendix (10 tables). 2 Indexes. Extensive bibliography. 31 tables. 97 figures. xxi + 644pp. 5⅜ x 8½.
S301 Paperbound **$3.00**

AN INTRODUCTORY TREATISE ON DYNAMICAL ASTRONOMY, H. C. Plummer. Unusually wide connected and concise coverage of nearly every significant branch of dynamical astronomy, stressing basic principles throughout: determination of orbits, planetary theory, lunar theory, precession and nutation, and many of their applications. Hundreds of formulas and theorems worked out completely, important methods thoroughly explained. Covers motion under a central attraction, orbits of double stars and spectroscopic binaries, the libration of the moon, and much more. Index. 8 diagrams. xxi + 343pp. 5⅝ x 8⅜.
S689 Paperbound **$2.35**

AN INTRODUCTORY TREATISE ON THE LUNAR THEORY, E. W. Brown. Indispensable for all scientists and engineers interested in orbital calculation, satellites, or navigation of space. Only work in English to explain in detail 5 major mathematical approaches to the problem of 3 bodies, those of Laplace, de Pontécoulant, Hansen, Delaunay, and Hill. Covers expressions for mutual attraction, equations of motion, forms of solution, variations of the elements in disturbed motion, the constants and their interpretations, planetary and other disturbing influences, etc. Index. Bibliography. Tables. xvi + 292pp. 5⅝ x 8⅜.
S666 Paperbound **$2.00**

SPHERICAL AND PRACTICAL ASTRONOMY, W. Chauvenet. First book in English to apply mathematical techniques to astronomical problems is still standard work. Covers almost entire field, rigorously, with over 300 examples worked out. Vol. 1, spherical astronomy, applications to nautical astronomy; determination of hour angles, parallactic angle for known stars; interpolation; parallax; laws of refraction; predicting eclipses; precession, nutation of fixed stars; etc. Vol. 2, theory, use, of instruments; telescope; measurement of arcs, angles in general; electro-chronograph; sextant, reflecting circles; zenith telescope; etc. 100-page appendix of detailed proof of Gauss' method of least squares. 5th revised edition. Index. 15 plates, 20 tables. 1340pp. 5⅜ x 8.
Vol. 1 S618 Paperbound **$2.75**
Vol. 2 S619 Paperbound **$2.75**
The set **$5.50**

RADIATIVE TRANSFER, S. Chandrasekhar. Definitive work in field provides foundation for analysis of stellar atmospheres, planetary illumination, sky radiation; to physicists, a study of problems analogous to those in theory of diffusion of neutrons. Partial contents: equation of transfer, isotropic scattering, H-functions, diffuse reflection and transmission, Rayleigh scattering, X, Y functions, radiative equilibrium of stellar atmospheres. Extensive bibliography. 3 appendices. 35 tables. 35 figures. 407pp. 5⅝ x 8⅜.
S599 Paperbound **$2.25**

PHILOSOPHY OF SCIENCE AND MATHEMATICS

FOUNDATIONS OF SCIENCE: THE PHILOSOPHY OF THEORY AND EXPERIMENT, N. R. Campbell.
A critique of the most fundamental concepts of science in general and physics in particular.
Examines why certain propositions are accepted without question, demarcates science from
philosophy, clarifies the understanding of the tools of science. Part One analyzes the pre-
suppositions of scientific thought: existence of the material world, nature of scientific
laws, multiplication of probabilities, etc.: Part Two covers the nature of experiment and the
application of mathematics: conditions for measurement, relations between numerical laws
and theories, laws of error, etc. An appendix covers problems arising from relativity, force,
motion, space, and time. A classic in its field. Index. xiii + 565pp. 5⅝ x 8⅜.
S372 Paperbound **$2.95**

THE NATURE OF PHYSICAL THEORY, P. W. Bridgman. Here is how modern physics looks to a
highly unorthodox physicist—a Nobel laureate. Pointing out many absurdities of science, and
demonstrating the inadequacies of various physical theories, Dr. Bridgman weighs and analyzes the contributions of Einstein, Bohr, Newton, Heisenberg, and many others. This is a
non-technical consideration of the correlation of science and reality. Index. xi + 138pp.
5⅜ x 8.
S33 Paperbound **$1.25**

THE VALUE OF SCIENCE, Henri Poincaré. Many of the most mature ideas of the "last scientific
universalist" covered with charm and vigor for both the beginning student and the advanced
worker. Discusses the nature of scientific truth, whether order is innate in the universe
or imposed upon it by man, logical thought versus intuition (relating to math, through the
works of Weierstrass, Lie, Klein, Riemann), time and space (relativity, psychological time,
simultaneity), Hertz's concept of force, interrelationship of mathematical physics to pure
math, values within disciplines of Maxwell, Carnot, Mayer, Newton, Lorentz, etc. Index.
iii + 147pp. 5⅜ x 8.
S469 Paperbound **$1.35**

SCIENCE AND HYPOTHESIS, Henri Poincaré. Creative psychology in science. How such concepts as number, magnitude, space, force, classical mechanics were developed, and how the
modern scientist uses them in his thought. Hypothesis in physics, theories of modern
physics. Introduction by Sir James Larmor. "Few mathematicians have had the breadth of
vision of Poincaré, and none is his superior in the gift of clear exposition," E. T. Bell.
Index. 272pp. 5⅜ x 8.
S221 Paperbound **$1.35**

PHILOSOPHY AND THE PHYSICISTS, L. S. Stebbing. The philosophical aspects of modern
science examined in terms of a lively critical attack on the ideas of Jeans and Eddington.
Discusses the task of science, causality, determinism, probability, consciousness, the relation
of the world of physics to that of everyday experience. Probes the philosophical significance
of the Planck-Bohr concept of discontinuous energy levels, the inferences to be drawn from
Heisenberg's Uncertainty Principle, the implications of "becoming" involved in the 2nd law
of thermodynamics, and other problems posed by the discarding of Laplacean determinism.
285pp. 5⅜ x 8.
T480 Paperbound **$1.65**

THE PHILOSOPHICAL WRITINGS OF PEIRCE, edited by Justus Buchler. (Formerly published as
THE PHILOSOPHY OF PEIRCE.) This is a carefully balanced exposition of Peirce's complete
system, written by Peirce himself. It covers such matters as scientific method, pure chance
vs. law, symbolic logic, theory of signs, pragmatism, experiment, and other topics. Introduction by Justus Buchler, Columbia University. xvi + 368pp. 5⅜ x 8.
T217 Paperbound **$2.00**

LANGUAGE, TRUTH AND LOGIC, A. Ayer. A clear introduction to the Vienna and Cambridge
schools of Logical Positivism. It sets up specific tests by which you can evaluate validity of
ideas, etc. Contents: Function of philosophy, elimination of metaphysics, nature of analysis,
a priori, truth and probability, etc. 10th printing. "I should like to have written it myself,"
Bertrand Russell. Index. 160pp. 5⅜ x 8.
T10 Paperbound **$1.25**

MATHEMATICS AND SCIENCE: LAST ESSAYS (DERNIÈRES PENSÉES), Henri Poincaré. Translated
by J. W. Bolduc. A posthumous volume of articles and lectures by the great French mathe-
matician, philosopher, scientist. Here are nine pieces, never before translated into English,
on such subjects as The Evolution of Laws, Space and Time, Space and 3 Dimensions, The
Logic of infinity in Mathematics (discussing Russell's theory of types), Mathematics and Logic,
The Quantum Theory and its Modern Applications, Relationship Between Matter and Ether,
Ethics and Science and The Moral Alliance. First English translation of Dernières Pensées.
New index. viii + 128pp. 5⅜ x 8½.
S1101 Paperbound **$1.25**

THE PSYCHOLOGY OF INVENTION IN THE MATHEMATICAL FIELD, J. Hadamard. Where do ideas
come from? What role does the unconscious play? Are ideas best developed by mathematical
reasoning, word reasoning, visualization? What are the methods used by Einstein, Poincaré,
Galton, Riemann? How can these techniques be applied by others? Hadamard, one of the
world's leading mathematicians, discusses these and other questions. xiii + 145pp. 5⅜ x 8.
T107 Paperbound **$1.25**

EXPERIMENT AND THEORY IN PHYSICS, Max Born. A Nobel laureate examines the nature and value of the counterclaims of experiment and theory in physics. Synthetic versus analytical scientific advances are analyzed in the work of Einstein, Bohr, Heisenberg, Planck, Eddington, Milne, and others by a fellow participant. 44pp. 5⅜ x 8. S308 Paperbound **75¢**

THE PHILOSOPHY OF SPACE AND TIME, H. Reichenbach. An important landmark in the development of the empiricist conception of geometry, covering the problem of the foundations of geometry, the theory of time, the consequences of Einstein's relativity, including: relations between theory and observations; coordinate and metrical properties of space; the psychological problem of visual intuition of non-Euclidean structures; and many other important topics in modern science and philosophy. The majority of ideas require only a knowledge of intermediate math. Introduction by R. Carnap. 49 figures. Index. xviii + 296pp. 5⅜ x 8. S443 Paperbound **$2.00**

OBSERVATION AND INTERPRETATION IN THE PHILOSOPHY OF PHYSICS: WITH SPECIAL REFERENCE TO QUANTUM MECHANICS, Edited by S. Körner. A collection of papers by philosophers and physicists arising out of a symposium held at Bristol, England in 1957 under the auspices of the Colston Research Society. One of the most important contributions to the philosophy of science in recent years. The discussions center around the adequacy or inadequacy of quantum mechanics in its orthodox formulations. Among the contributors are A. J. Ayer, D. Bohm, K. Popper, F. Bopp, S. Körner, J. P. Vigier, M. Polanyi, P. K. Feyerabend, W. C. Kneale. W. B. Gallie, G. Ryle, Sir Charles Darwin, and R. B. Braithwaite. xiv + 218pp. 5⅜ x 8½. S131 Paperbound **$1.60**

SPACE AND TIME IN CONTEMPORARY PHYSICS: AN INTRODUCTION TO THE THEORY OF RELATIVITY AND GRAVITATION, Moritz Schlick. Exposition of the theory of relativity by the leader of the famed "Vienna Circle." Its essential purpose is to describe the physical doctrines of special and general relativity with particular reference to their philosophical significance. Explanations of such topics as the geometrical relativity of space, the connection with inertia and gravitation, the measure-determination of the space-time continuum, the finite universe, etc., with their philosophical ramifications. Index. xii + 89pp. 5⅜ x 8½. T1008 Paperbound **$1.00**

SUBSTANCE AND FUNCTION, & EINSTEIN'S THEORY OF RELATIVITY, Ernst Cassirer. Two books bound as one. Cassirer establishes a philosophy of the exact sciences that takes into consideration newer developments in mathematics, and also shows historical connections. Partial contents: Aristotelian logic, Mill's analysis, Helmholtz & Kronecker, Russell & cardinal numbers, Euclidean vs. non-Euclidean geometry, Einstein's relativity. Bibliography. Index. xxi + 465pp. 5⅜ x 8. T50 Paperbound **$2.25**

PRINCIPLES OF MECHANICS, Heinrich Hertz. This last work by the great 19th century physicist is not only a classic, but of great interest in the logic of science. Creating a new system of mechanics based upon space, time, and mass, it returns to axiomatic analysis, to understanding of the formal or structural aspects of science, taking into account logic, observation, and a priori elements. Of great historical importance to Poincaré, Carnap, Einstein, Milne. A 20-page introduction by R. S. Cohen, Wesleyan University, analyzes the implications of Hertz's thought and the logic of science. Bibliography. 13-page introduction by Helmholtz. xlii + 274pp. 5⅜ x 8. S316 Clothbound **$3.50**
S317 Paperbound **$1.85**

THE ANALYSIS OF MATTER, Bertrand Russell. How do our senses concord with the new physics? This volume covers such topics as logical analysis of physics, prerelativity physics, causality, scientific inference, physics and perception, special and general relativity, Weyl's theory, tensors, invariants and their physical interpretation, periodicity and qualitative series. "The most thorough treatment of the subject that has yet been published," THE NATION. Introduction by L. E. Denonn. 422pp. 5⅜ x 8. T231 Paperbound **$1.95**

FOUNDATIONS OF GEOMETRY, Bertrand Russell. Analyzing basic problems in the overlap area between mathematics and philosophy, Nobel laureate Russell examines the nature of geometrical knowledge, the nature of geometry, and the application of geometry to space. It covers the history of non-Euclidean geometry, philosophic interpretations of geometry—especially Kant—projective and metrical geometry. This is most interesting as the solution offered in 1897 by a great mind to a problem still current. New introduction by Prof. Morris Kline of N. Y. University. xii + 201pp. 5⅜ x 8. S232 Clothbound **$3.25**
S233 Paperbound **$1.75**

IDENTITY AND REALITY, Emile Meyerson. Called by Einstein a "brilliant study in the theory of knowledge," this book by the renowned Franco-German thinker is a major treatise in the philosophy of science and epistemology. Thorough, critical inquiries into causality, scientific laws, conservation of matter and energy, the unity of matter, Carnot's principle, the irrational, the elimination of time. Searches out the solutions of epistemological questions that form the bases of the scientific method. Authorized translation by Kate Loewenberg. Author's prefaces. Editor's preface. Appendices. Index. 495pp. 5⅜ x 8½. T65 Paperbound **$2.25**

ESSAYS IN EXPERIMENTAL LOGIC, John Dewey. This stimulating series of essays touches upon the relationship between inquiry and experience, dependence of knowledge upon thought, character of logic; judgments of practice, data and meanings, stimuli of thought, etc. Index. viii + 444pp. 5⅜ x 8. T73 Paperbound **$1.95**

ENGINEERING AND TECHNOLOGY

General and mathematical

ENGINEERING MATHEMATICS, Kenneth S. Miller. A text for graduate students of engineering to strengthen their mathematical background in differential equations, etc. Mathematical steps very explicitly indicated. Contents: Determinants and Matrices, Integrals, Linear Differential Equations, Fourier Series and Integrals, Laplace Transform, Network Theory, Random Function . . . all vital requisites for advanced modern engineering studies. Unabridged republication. Appendices: Borel Sets; Riemann-Stieltjes Integral; Fourier Series and Integrals. Index. References at Chapter Ends. xii + 417pp. 6 x 8½.   S1121 Paperbound **$2.00**

MATHEMATICAL ENGINEERING ANALYSIS, Rufus Oldenburger. A book designed to assist the research engineer and scientist in making the transition from physical engineering situations to the corresponding mathematics. Scores of common practical situations found in all major fields of physics are supplied with their correct mathematical formulations—applications to automobile springs and shock absorbers, clocks, throttle torque of diesel engines, resistance networks, capacitors, transmission lines, microphones, neon tubes, gasoline engines, refrigeration cycles, etc. Each section reviews basic principles of underlying various fields: mechanics of rigid bodies, electricity and magnetism, heat, elasticity, fluid mechanics, and aerodynamics. Comprehensive and eminently useful. Index. 169 problems, answers. 200 photos and diagrams. xiv + 426pp. 5⅜ x 8½.   S919 Paperbound **$2.00**

MATHEMATICS OF MODERN ENGINEERING, E. G. Keller and R. E. Doherty. Written for the Advanced Course in Engineering of the General Electric Corporation, deals with the engineering use of determinants, tensors, the Heaviside operational calculus, dyadics, the calculus of variations, etc. Presents underlying principles fully, but purpose is to teach engineers to deal with modern engineering problems, and emphasis is on the perennial engineering attack of set-up and solve. Indexes. Over 185 figures and tables. Hundreds of exercises, problems, and worked-out examples. References. Two volume set. Total of xxxiii + 623pp. 5⅜ x 8.

S734 Vol I Paperbound **$1.85**
S735 Vol II Paperbound **$1.85**
The set **$3.70**

MATHEMATICAL METHODS FOR SCIENTISTS AND ENGINEERS, L. P. Smith. For scientists and engineers, as well as advanced math students. Full investigation of methods and practical description of conditions under which each should be used. Elements of real functions, differential and integral calculus, space geometry, theory of residues, vector and tensor analysis, series of Bessel functions, etc. Each method illustrated by completely-worked-out examples, mostly from scientific literature. 368 graded unsolved problems. 100 diagrams. x + 453pp. 5⅝ x 8⅜.   S220 Paperbound **$2.00**

THEORY OF FUNCTIONS AS APPLIED TO ENGINEERING PROBLEMS, edited by R. Rothe, F. Ollendorff, and K. Pohlhausen. A series of lectures given at the Berlin Institute of Technology that shows the specific applications of function theory in electrical and allied fields of engineering. Six lectures provide the elements of function theory in a simple and practical form, covering complex quantities and variables, integration in the complex plane, residue theorems, etc. Then 5 lectures show the exact uses of this powerful mathematical tool, with full discussions of problem methods. Index. Bibliography. 108 figures. x + 189pp. 5⅜ x 8.

S733 Paperbound **$1.35**

Aerodynamics and hydrodynamics

AIRPLANE STRUCTURAL ANALYSIS AND DESIGN, E. E. Sechler and L. G. Dunn. Systematic authoritative book which summarizes a large amount of theoretical and experimental work on structural analysis and design. Strong on classical subsonic material still basic to much aeronautic design . . . remains a highly useful source of information. Covers such areas as layout of the airplane, applied and design loads, stress-strain relationships for stable structures, truss and frame analysis, the problem of instability, the ultimate strength of stiffened flat sheet, analysis of cylindrical structures, wings and control surfaces, fuselage analysis, engine mounts, landing gears, etc. Originally published as part of the CALCIT Aeronautical Series. 256 Illustrations. 47 study problems. Indexes. xi + 420pp. 5⅜ x 8½.

S1043 Paperbound **$2.25**

FUNDAMENTALS OF HYDRO- AND AEROMECHANICS, L. Prandtl and O. G. Tietjens. The well-known standard work based upon Prandtl's lectures at Goettingen. Wherever possible hydrodynamics theory is referred to practical considerations in hydraulics, with the view of unifying theory and experience. Presentation is extremely clear and though primarily physical, mathematical proofs are rigorous and use vector analysis to a considerable extent. An Engineering Society Monograph, 1934. 186 figures. Index. xvi + 270pp. 5⅜ x 8.

S374 Paperbound **$1.85**

CHEMISTRY AND PHYSICAL CHEMISTRY

ORGANIC CHEMISTRY, F. C. Whitmore. The entire subject of organic chemistry for the practicing chemist and the advanced student. Storehouse of facts, theories, processes found elsewhere only in specialized journals. Covers aliphatic compounds (500 pages on the properties and synthetic preparation of hydrocarbons, halides, proteins, ketones, etc.), alicyclic compounds, aromatic compounds, heterocyclic compounds, organophosphorus and organometallic compounds. Methods of synthetic preparation analyzed critically throughout. Includes much of biochemical interest. "The scope of this volume is astonishing," INDUSTRIAL AND ENGINEERING CHEMISTRY. 12,000-reference index. 2387-item bibliography. Total of x + 1005pp. 5⅜ x 8.
Two volume set.
S700 Vol I Paperbound **$2.00**
S701 Vol II Paperbound **$2.00**
The set **$4.00**

THE MODERN THEORY OF MOLECULAR STRUCTURE, Bernard Pullman. A reasonably popular account of recent developments in atomic and molecular theory. Contents: The Wave Function and Wave Equations (history and bases of present theories of molecular structure); The Electronic Structure of Atoms (Description and classification of atomic wave functions, etc.); Diatomic Molecules; Non-Conjugated Polyatomic Molecules; Conjugated Polyatomic Molecules; The Structure of Complexes. Minimum of mathematical background needed. New translation by David Antin of "La Structure Moleculaire." Index. Bibliography. vii + 87pp. 5⅜ x 8½.
S987 Paperbound **$1.00**

CATALYSIS AND CATALYSTS, Marcel Prettre, Director, Research Institute on Catalysis. This brief book, translated into English for the first time, is the finest summary of the principal modern concepts, methods, and results of catalysis. Ideal introduction for beginning chemistry and physics students. Chapters: Basic Definitions of Catalysis (true catalysis and generalization of the concept of catalysis); The Scientific Bases of Catalysis (Catalysis and chemical thermodynamics, catalysis and chemical kinetics); Homogeneous Catalysis (acid-base catalysis, etc.); Chain Reactions; Contact Masses; Heterogeneous Catalysis (Mechanisms of contact catalyses, etc.); and Industrial Applications (acids and fertilizers, petroleum and petroleum chemistry, rubber, plastics, synthetic resins, and fibers). Translated by David Antin. Index. vi + 88pp. 5⅜ x 8½.
S998 Paperbound **$1.00**

POLAR MOLECULES, Pieter Debye. This work by Nobel laureate Debye offers a complete guide to fundamental electrostatic field relations, polarizability, molecular structure. Partial contents: electric intensity, displacement and force, polarization by orientation, molar polarization and molar refraction, halogen-hydrides, polar liquids, ionic saturation, dielectric constant, etc. Special chapter considers quantum theory. Indexed. 172pp. 5⅜ x 8.
S64 Paperbound **$1.50**

THE ELECTRONIC THEORY OF ACIDS AND BASES, W. F. Luder and Saverio Zuffanti. The first full systematic presentation of the electronic theory of acids and bases—treating the theory and its ramifications in an uncomplicated manner. Chapters: Historical Background; Atomic Orbitals and Valence; The Electronic Theory of Acids and Bases; Electrophilic and Electrodotic Reagents; Acidic and Basic Radicals; Neutralization; Titrations with Indicators; Displacement; Catalysis; Acid Catalysis; Base Catalysis; Alkoxides and Catalysts; Conclusion. Required reading for all chemists. Second revised (1961) eidtion, with additional examples and references. 3 figures. 9 tables. Index. Bibliography xii + 165pp. 5⅜ x 8.
S201 Paperbound **$1.50**

KINETIC THEORY OF LIQUIDS, J. Frenkel. Regarding the kinetic theory of liquids as a generalization and extension of the theory of solid bodies, this volume covers all types of arrangements of solids, thermal displacements of atoms, interstitial atoms and ions, orientational and rotational motion of molecules, and transition between states of matter. Mathematical theory is developed close to the physical subject matter. 216 bibliographical footnotes. 55 figures. xi + 485pp. 5⅜ x 8.
S95 Paperbound **$2.55**

THE PRINCIPLES OF ELECTROCHEMISTRY, D. A. MacInnes. Basic equations for almost every subfield of electrochemistry from first principles, referring at all times to the soundest and most recent theories and results; unusually useful as text or as reference. Covers coulometers and Faraday's Law, electrolytic conductance, the Debye-Hueckel method for the theoretical calculation of activity coefficients, concentration cells, standard electrode potentials, thermodynamic ionization constants, pH, potentiometric titrations, irreversible phenomena, Planck's equation, and much more. "Excellent treatise," AMERICAN CHEMICAL SOCIETY JOURNAL. "Highly recommended," CHEMICAL AND METALLURGICAL ENGINEERING. 2 Indices. Appendix. 585-item bibliography. 137 figures. 94 tables. ii + 478pp. 5⅝ x 8⅜.
S52 Paperbound **$2.45**

THE PHASE RULE AND ITS APPLICATION, Alexander Findlay. Covering chemical phenomena of 1, 2, 3, 4, and multiple component systems, this "standard work on the subject" (NATURE, London), has been completely revised and brought up to date by A. N. Campbell and N. O. Smith. Brand new material has been added on such matters as binary, tertiary liquid equilibria, solid solutions in ternary systems, quinary systems of salts and water. Completely revised to triangular coordinates in ternary systems, clarified graphic representation, solid models, etc. 9th revised edition. Author, subject indexes. 236 figures. 505 footnotes, mostly bibliographic. xii + 494pp. 5⅜ x 8.
S91 Paperbound **$2.45**

Catalogue of Dover Books

THE SOLUBILITY OF NONELECTROLYTES, Joel H. Hildebrand and Robert L. Scott. The standard work on the subject; still indispensable as a reference source and for classroom work. Partial contents: The Ideal Solution (including Raoult's Law and Henry's Law, etc.); Nonideal Solutions; Intermolecular Forces; The Liquid State; Entropy of Athermal Mixing; Heat of Mixing; Polarity; Hydrogen Bonding; Specific Interactions; "Solvation" and "Association"; Systems of Three or More Components; Vapor Pressure of Binary Liquid Solutions; Mixtures of Gases; Solubility of Gases in Liquids; of Liquids in Liquids; of Solids in Liquids; Evaluation of Solubility Parameters; and other topics. Corrected republication of third (revised) edition. Appendices. Indexes. 138 figures. 111 tables. 1 photograph. iv + 488pp. 5⅜ x 8½.
S1125 Paperbound **$2.50**

TERNARY SYSTEMS: INTRODUCTION TO THE THEORY OF THREE COMPONENT SYSTEMS, G. Masing. Furnishes detailed discussion of representative types of 3-components systems, both in solid models (particularly metallic alloys) and isothermal models. Discusses mechanical mixture without compounds and without solid solutions; unbroken solid solution series; solid solutions with solubility breaks in two binary systems; iron-silicon-aluminum alloys; allotropic forms of iron in ternary system; other topics. Bibliography. Index. 166 illustrations. 178pp. 5⅝ x 8⅜.
S631 Paperbound **$1.50**

THE KINETIC THEORY OF GASES, Leonard B. Loeb, University of California. Comprehensive text and reference book which presents full coverage of basic theory and the important experiments and developments in the field for the student and investigator. Partial contents: The Mechanical Picture of a Perfect Gas, The Mean Free Path—Clausius' Deductions, Distribution of Molecular Velocities, discussions of theory of the problem of specific heats, the contributions of kinetic theory to our knowledge of electrical and magnetic properties of molecules and its application to the conduction of electricity in gases. New 14-page preface to Dover edition by the author. Name, subject indexes. Six appendices. 570-item bibliography. xxxvi + 687pp. 5⅜ x 8½.
S942 Paperbound **$2.95**

IONS IN SOLUTION, Ronald W. Gurney. A thorough and readable introduction covering all the fundamental principles and experiments in the field, by an internationally-known authority. Contains discussions of solvation energy, atomic and molecular ions, lattice energy, transferral of ions, interionic forces, cells and half-cells, transference of electrons, exchange forces, hydrogen ions, the electro-chemical series, and many other related topics. Indispensable to advanced undergraduates and graduate students in electrochemistry. Index. 45 illustrations. 15 tables. vii + 206pp. 5⅜ x 8½.
S124 Paperbound **$1.50**

IONIC PROCESSES IN SOLUTION, Ronald W. Gurney. Lucid, comprehensive examination which brings together the approaches of electrochemistry, thermodynamics, statistical mechanics, electroacoustics, molecular physics, and quantum theory in the interpretation of the behavior of ionic solutions—the most important single work on the subject. More extensive and technical than the author's earlier work (IONS IN SOLUTION), it is a middle-level text for graduate students and researchers in electrochemistry. Covers such matters as Brownian motion in liquids, molecular ions in solution, heat of precipitation, entropy of solution, proton transfers, dissociation constant of nitric acid, viscosity of ionic solutions, etc. 78 illustrations. 47 tables. Name and subject index. ix + 275pp. 5⅜ x 8½.
S134 Paperbound **$1.75**

CRYSTALLOGRAPHIC DATA ON METAL AND ALLOY STRUCTURES, Compiled by A. Taylor and B. J. Kagle, Westinghouse Research Laboratories. Unique collection of the latest crystallographic data on alloys, compounds, and the elements, with lattice spacings expressed uniformly in absolute Angstrom units. Gathers together previously widely-scattered data from the Power Data File of the ATSM, structure reports, and the Landolt-Bornstein Tables, as well as from other original literature. 2300 different compounds listed in the first table. Alloys and Intermetallic Compounds, with much vital information on each. Also listings for nearly 700 Borides, Carbides, Hydrides, Oxides, Nitrides. Also all the necessary data on the crystal structure of 77 elements. vii + 263pp. 5⅜ x 8.
S1013 Paperbound **$2.25**

MATHEMATICAL CRYSTALLOGRAPHY AND THE THEORY OF GROUPS OF MOVEMENTS, Harold Hilton. Classic account of the mathematical theory of crystallography, particularly the geometrical theory of crystal-structure based on the work of Bravais, Jordan, Sohncke, Federow, Schoenflies, and Barlow. Partial contents: The Stereographic Projection, Properties Common to Symmetrical and Asymmetrical Crystals, The Theory of Groups, Coordinates of Equivalent Points, Crystallographic Axes and Axial Ratios, The Forms and Growth of Crystals, Lattices and Translations, The Structure-Theory, Infinite Groups of Movements, Triclinic and Monoclinic Groups, Orthorhombic Groups, etc. Index. 188 figures. xii + 262pp. 5⅜ x 8½.
S1058 Paperbound **$2.00**

CLASSICS IN THE THEORY OF CHEMICAL COMBINATIONS. Edited by O. T. Benfey. Vol. I of the Classics of Science Series, G. Holton, Harvard University, General Editor. This book is a collection of papers representing the major chapters in the development of the valence concept in chemistry. Includes essays by Wöhler and Liebig, Laurent, Williamson, Frankland, Kekulé and Couper, and two by van't Hoff and le Bel, which mark the first extension of the valence concept beyond its purely numerical character. Introduction and epilogue by Prof. Benfey. Index. 9 illustrations. New translation of Kekulé paper by Benfey. xiv + 191pp. 5⅜ x 8½.
S1066 Paperbound **$1.85**

THE CHEMISTRY OF URANIUM: THE ELEMENT, ITS BINARY AND RELATED COMPOUNDS, J. J. Katz and E. Rabinowitch. Vast post-World War II collection and correlation of thousands of AEC reports and published papers in a useful and easily accessible form, still the most complete and up-to-date compilation. Treats "dry uranium chemistry," occurrences, preparation, properties, simple compounds, isotopic composition, extraction from ores, spectra, alloys, etc. Much material available only here. Index. Thousands of evaluated bibliographical references. 324 tables, charts, figures. xxi + 609pp. 5⅜ x 8.   S757 Paperbound **$2.95**

THE STORY OF ALCHEMY AND EARLY CHEMISTRY, J. M. Stillman. An authoritative, scholarly work, highly readable, of development of chemical knowledge from 4000 B.C. to downfall of phlogiston theory in late 18th century. Every important figure, many quotations. Brings alive curious, almost incredible history of alchemical beliefs, practices, writings of Arabian Prince Oneeyade, Vincent of Beauvais, Geber, Zosimos, Paracelsus, Vitruvius, scores more. Studies work, thought of Black, Cavendish, Priestley, Van Helmont, Bergman, Lavoisier, Newton, etc. Index. Bibliography. 579pp. 5⅜ x 8.   S628 Paperbound **$2.45**

Prices subject to change without notice.

Dover publishes books on art, music, philosophy, literature, languages, history, social sciences, psychology, handcrafts, orientalia, puzzles and entertainments, chess, pets and gardens, books explaining science, intermediate and higher mathematics, mathematical physics, engineering, biological sciences, earth sciences, classics of science, etc. Write to:

Dept. catrr.
Dover Publications, Inc.
180 Varick Street, N.Y. 14, N.Y.

(continued from front flap)

The Theory of Optics, Paul Drude. $2.45

Hydrodynamics, Hugh L. Dryden, Francis D. Murnaghan, and Harry Bateman. $2.75

Aerodynamic Theory, William F. Durand, editor-in-chief. Clothbound. Three volume set $17.50

Mathematical Tables of Elementary and Some Higher Mathematical Functions, Herbert B. Dwight. $1.75

Investigations on the Theory of the Brownian Movement, Albert Einstein. $1.25

The Principle of Relativity, Albert Einstein. Hendrik A. Lorentz, Hermann Minkowski and Hermann Weyl. $1.75

The Story of Atomic Theory and Atomic Energy, J. G. Feinberg. $1.45

Thermodynamics, Enrico Fermi. $1.75

Die Differential- und Integralgleichungen der Mechanik und Physik, Philipp Frank and Richard von Mises. Clothbound. Two volume set $15.00

Kinetic Theory of Liquids, J. Frenkel. $2.55

Scientific Papers of J. Willard Gibbs. Two volume set $4.00

Vector Analysis, Founded Upon the Lectures of J. Willard Gibbs, E. B. Wilson. $2.25

Elementary Principles in Statistical Mechanics, J. Willard Gibbs. $1.45

A Treatise on Gyrostatics and Rotational Motion, Andrew Gray. $2.75

Vector and Tensor Analysis, G. E. Hay. $1.75

The Physical Principles of the Quantum Theory, Werner Heisenberg. $1.25

A Treatise on Physiological Optics, Hermann von Helmholtz. Clothbound. Three volume set $15.00

On the Sensations of Tone, Hermann von Helmholtz. $3.00

Electric Waves, Heinrich Hertz. $1.75

Principles of Mechanics, Heinrich Hertz. Paperbound $1.85

Paperbound unless otherwise indicated. Prices subject to change without notice. Available at your book dealer or write for free catalogues to Dept. TF 1, Dover Publications, Inc., 180 Varick St., N. Y., N .Y. 10014. Please indicate field of interest. Dover publishes over 150 new books and records each year on mathematics, introductory science, chemistry, puzzles, chess, languages, philosophy, art, classical records, and other areas.

MAGNETISM AND VERY LOW TEMPERATURES

By H. B. G. Casimir

Philips Research Laboratories, Eindhoven, Holland

This concise and authoritative study by one of the world's great physicists has become a basic work in the literature of low temperature physics. Students of the subject and working scientists find it equally helpful, for it not only provides a survey of fundamental theoretical principles, but also points out promising lines of experimental investigation.

Opening with a discussion of the methods for obtaining very low temperatures, Dr. Casimir describes the process of adiabatic demagnetization and details the most important experiments in this line from 1926 on. He then covers the important elements of classical theory for the benefit of the student, deriving the field equations for a magnetic substance and studying basic thermodynamic relations. The most useful experimental methods are classified and described as well: magnetic balances, magnetometers, induction methods, ballistic methods, and A.C. methods.

Chapter III deals with the quantum theory of paramagnetism covering the Hamiltonian function, magnetism due to electron spins, and the influence of splittings. Chapter IV returns to adiabatic demagnetization to describe how entropy and specific heat of a substance can be derived from magnetic measurements.

In the final chapters, the author performs the extremely valuable service of describing and relating the most important experiments performed so far, and showing what elements of theory are left unsubstantiated by experiment. In this section he covers Kramers' theorem, the Lorentz field, Onsager's theory, Stark splitting, the low-temperature properties of various substances, and relaxation phenomena.

Republication of 1st (1940) edition. Index. 89-item bibliography. ix + 95pp. 5⅜ x 8. S943 Paperbound $1.35

A DOVER EDITION DESIGNED FOR YEARS OF USE!

We have made every effort to make this the best book possible. Our paper is opaque, with min   iscolor or become brittle with age. Pages   ethod traditionally used for the best books,   happens with paperbacks held together with   erence. The binding will not crack or split. This is a permanent book.